OCR Additional Mathematics
Practice Book

Val Hanrahan

Hachette UK's policy is to use papers that are natural, renewable and recyclable products and made from wood grown in sustainable forests. The logging and manufacturing processes are expected to conform to the environmental regulations of the country of origin.

Orders: please contact Bookpoint Ltd, 130 Milton Park, Abingdon, Oxon OX14 4SB.

Telephone: (44) 01235 827720. Fax: (44) 01235 400454. Lines are open 9.00–5.00, Monday to Saturday, with a 24-hour message answering service. Visit our website at www.hoddereducation.co.uk

First published in 2013 by

Hodder Education, an Hachette UK company,
Carmelite House, 50 Victoria Embankment,
London EC4Y 0DZ

Impression number 7

Year 2018

Illustrations by Integra Software Services Pvt. Ltd.

Typeset in India by Integra Software Services Pvt. Ltd.

Printed in Great Britain by CPI Group (UK) Ltd, Croydon, CR0 4YY

A catalogue record for this title is available from the British Library

ISBN 978 1444 189506

Contents

SECTION 2   Co-ordinate geometry

SECTION 3   Trigonometry

SECTION 4   Calculus

Introduction

This book has been written to supplement the *Additional Mathematics for OCR* textbook, but it could also be used to provide additional exercises for anyone studying Mathematics beyond GCSE. It covers topics in Algebra, Co-ordinate Geometry, Trigonometry and Calculus, together with applications of the techniques introduced in those sections.

Each chapter starts by summarising the formulae that are relevant to the section – identifying those which need to learnt, and these are followed by detailed Key points which include brief examples where appropriate.

Each chapter contains questions set at three levels. **Level 1** questions are short, direct applications of the theory. **Level 2** questions are slightly longer and less straightforward, but nevertheless are still focused directly on the topic in the chapter. **Level 3** questions are more demanding.

A few of the most challenging questions are followed by this symbol: 💡. This indicates that there is a suggestion to help you answer the question in the Hints section at the back of the book.

Not all of the exercises in this book are the same length, as the questions have been carefully chosen to ensure they provide complete coverage of the skills you may need to demonstrate within each section. Therefore, you can use these exercises to assess your understanding of each topic.

I have not set out to provide large numbers of repetitive questions, as students often prepare for this qualification within a very limited period of time.

This book has been written in response to requests from teachers asking for a small, homework-style practice book to accompany the *Additional Mathematics for OCR* textbook. I hope that I have fulfilled these expectations, and that students will find this a useful addition to the series.

I would like to thank Hodder Education for asking me to write this book, and Elaine Lambert in particular for the helpful suggestions that she has made. Once again, thanks to my own students who have unwittingly trialled some of the material.

Val Hanrahan

SECTION 1
Algebra

Algebra I – review

Formulae you need to learn

- The quadratic equation $ax^2 + bx + c = 0$ has roots given by $x = \dfrac{-b \pm \sqrt{b^2 - 4ac}}{2a}$.

- One root is found by taking the + sign and the other by taking the – sign.

Basic algebra

LEVEL 1

1 Simplify the following expressions.

(i) $2x + y - x + 5y$ (ii) $2x + 3y - (x - y)$

(iii) $5a + 2b - (a - 3b)$

2 Multiply out the following expressions.

(i) $3(x + y) + 2(y - x)$ (ii) $5a(a + 3) - 2a(a - 2)$

(iii) $2p(p^2 - 1) - p^2(p + 1)$

3 Factorise the following expressions fully.

(i) $6x + 10x^2$ (ii) $3ab^2 - 9a^2b$ (iii) $12pq^2 - 3p^4q$

4 Simplify the following expressions as much as possible.

(i) $ab \times 2bc \times 3ac$ (ii) $3x^2y \times 4xy^4$ (iii) $5x^3y^2 \div 10xy^5$

(iv) $\dfrac{2pq}{r^2} \times \dfrac{3pr}{4q^2}$ (v) $\dfrac{3a^2}{8bc^2} \div \dfrac{9ab}{2c^2}$

5 Simplify the following expressions by writing them as a single fraction.

(i) $\dfrac{5x}{2} + \dfrac{3x}{4}$ (ii) $\dfrac{3s}{2} - \dfrac{s-1}{4}$ (iii) $\dfrac{5a}{3b} - \dfrac{3a}{5b}$

6 Solve the following equations.

(i) $2(x - 2) = (4 + x)$ (ii) $\dfrac{p-1}{3} + \dfrac{p}{2} = \dfrac{13}{6}$

LEVEL 2

7 Make t the subject of each of the following formulae.

(i) $2t + 3s = 2(2t - s)$ (ii) $s = \dfrac{(u+v)}{2}t$ (iii) $\dfrac{a+t}{2} = \dfrac{t-a}{3}$

8 In 21 years' time, Martin will be seven times as old as he was 3 years ago.

(i) Write this information in the form of an equation involving Martin's present age, a years.

(ii) Solve this equation to find Martin's present age.

9 The largest angle of a triangle is 5 times as big as the smallest angle, and the third angle is 78°.

(i) Write this information in the form of an equation in θ, the size in degrees of the smallest angle.

(ii) Solve this equation and find the sizes of the three angles.

LEVEL 3

10 One rectangle has a length of $(x+4)$ cm and a breadth of 3 cm, and another of equal area has a length of $(x-2)$ cm and a breadth of 5 cm.

(i) Write down an equation in x and solve it.

(ii) What is the area of each rectangle?

11 In a multiple choice examination of 20 questions, four marks are given for a correct answer, two marks are deducted for each wrong answer, and one mark is deducted for any question which is not attempted. A candidate attempts q questions and gets c correct.

(i) Write down an expression for the candidate's total marks in terms of q and c.

Mollie attempts 18 questions and scores 52 marks.

(ii) Write down and solve an equation for the number of questions she solves correctly.

EXERCISE 1.2

Quadratic expressions and equations

LEVEL 1

1 Expand the following expressions.

(i) $(a+2)(a-3)$ (ii) $(3x-2)(x+4)$ (iii) $(5-2x)^2$

2 Factorise the following expressions.

(i) $a^2+7a+10$ (ii) x^2-x-12 (iii) p^2-4

(iv) $9-4t^2$ (v) $2c^2-3c-2$ (vi) $3x^2-8x-3$

3 Factorise the following expressions completely.

(i) $2x^2-18$ (ii) a^3-9a^2+20a

(iii) $ab^3+2a^2b^2+a^3b$

4 Solve the following equations by factorising.

(i) $x^2-9x+20=0$ (ii) $4a^2+a=18$

5 Solve the following equations by completing the square. Leave your answers in surd form.

(i) $x^2 + 2x = 1$ (ii) $a^2 - 6a - 12 = 0$

6 Solve the following equations by using the quadratic formula. Give your answers correct to 2 decimal places.

(i) $x^2 + 2x - 7 = 0$ (ii) $2x^2 + x - 2 = 0$

7 Use a suitable method to solve the following equations.

(i) $3a^2 - 14a + 8 = 0$ (ii) $x^2 + 8x = 14$ (iii) $3p^2 + 2p - 3 = 0$

8 (i) Express $f(x) = 4x^2 + 2x - 3$ in the form $(2x + a)^2 - b$.

(ii) Hence find the minimum value of $f(x)$ and the value of x when this occurs.

LEVEL 3

9 The height h metres of a ball at a time t seconds after it is thrown up in the air is given by the expression $h = 1 + 20t - 5t^2$.

(i) Find the times at which the height is 16 m.

(ii) How long does the ball take to return to the thrower if it is caught at the same height?

The thrower fails to catch the ball.

(iii) Find, to 2 decimal places, the value of t when the ball reaches the ground.

10 Jennie is making a patchwork quilt from square patches and she has already made 165 patches.

(i) If she sews these in n equal rows, write down an expression for the number of patches in each row. If she makes 15 more patches, she could have had three more rows, but with one patch less in each row.

(ii) Explain why $(n + 3)\left(\dfrac{165}{n} - 1\right) = 180$.

(iii) Show that this equation can be written as $n^2 + 18n - 495 = 0$.

(iv) Solve this equation to find the value of n.

11 Anna and Ammarah are carrying out an experiment and the table below shows their results.

x	0	1	2	3
y	6	0	2	0

Anna proposes that the relationship should be modelled by $y = c(x-1)(x-3)$.

(i) Find the value of c for which the points $(0, 6)$, $(1, 0)$ and $(3, 0)$ satisfy this equation.

(ii) Sketch the curve for this relationship.

Ammarah proposes a different model using $y = k(x-1)^2(x-3)$.

(iii) Find the value of k for which the points $(0, 6)$, $(1, 0)$ and $(3, 0)$ satisfy this equation.

(iv) Which is the better model? Give a reason for your answer.

EXERCISE 1.3 # Simultaneous equations

LEVEL 1

1 Solve the following pairs of simultaneous equations using the substitution method.

(i) $x + 2y = 3$
$y = x + 1$

(ii) $3x + y = 13$
$x = y + 1$

2 Solve the following pairs of simultaneous equations using the elimination method.

(i) $2x + y = 5$
$x + 2y = 1$

(ii) $3x + 4y = 11$
$4x + 3y = 10$

3 Solve the following pairs of simultaneous equations using a suitable method.

(i) $y = 3x + 2$
$x^2 + y^2 = 26$

(ii) $2x + y + 3 = 0$
$x^2 + 2y + y^2 = 16$

LEVEL 2

4 Find the points of intersection of the line $y = 2x - 3$ with the circle $x^2 + y^2 = 16$, giving your answer correct to 2 decimal places.

5 The cost of 2 kg of apples and 3 kg of pears is £6.60. The cost of 3 kg of apples and 5 kg of pears is £10.60. Work out the cost of 4 kg of apples and 1 kg of pears.

6 Show that the simultaneous equations $3x - 2y = 4$ and $6x = 4y - 12$ have no solution. Why does this happen?

LEVEL 3

7 Two positive numbers differ by 4 and have a product of 10. Find the two numbers to 2 decimal places. 💡

2

Algebra II – techniques

Formulae you need to learn

There are no formulae that you need to learn for this section.

- Linear inequalities are dealt with like equations *but* if you multiply or divide by a negative number you must reverse the inequality sign.

For example:

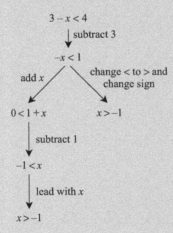

$3 - x < 4$

↓ subtract 3

$-x < 1$

add x / change < to > and change sign

$0 < 1 + x$ $x > -1$

↓ subtract 1

$-1 < x$

↓ lead with x

$x > -1$

- When representing an inequality on a number line, use a solid circle ● at the end of the line if that point is included in the solution, and an open circle ○ if it is not.

- When solving a quadratic inequality there are two possible methods (both in the text book) but it is generally advisable to sketch the graph, no matter which method you use.

- When the solution to a quadratic inequality is illustrated in the form of two separate line segments, then the algebraic answer will be two separate inequalities. These cannot be combined into a single statement.

For example:

To solve $(x-3)(x+1) > 0$

Sketch the graph $y = (x-3)(x+1)$ and find values of x where $y > 0$.

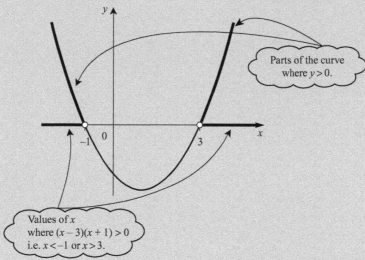

Parts of the curve where $y > 0$.

Values of x where $(x-3)(x+1) > 0$ i.e. $x < -1$ or $x > 3$.

■ When simplifying an algebraic fraction involving multiplication or division, you should factorise where possible first and then you can cancel by any common factors.

■ When simplifying an algebraic fraction involving addition or subtraction you need to find a common denominator. The smallest common denominator will be the least common multiple (LCM) of the existing denominators.

For example:

$$\frac{3}{2a^3} - \frac{5}{8a^2}$$

LCM of 2 and 8 is 8

LCM of a^3 and a^2 is a^3

$\Rightarrow$ common denominator is $8a^3$

$$= \frac{3 \times 4}{2a^3 \times 4} - \frac{5 \times a}{8a^2 \times a}$$

$$= \frac{12}{8a^3} - \frac{5a}{8a^3}$$

$$= \frac{12 - 5a}{8a^3}.$$

■ When solving an equation involving algebraic fractions it is best to start by multiplying through by the LCM of all the denominators to eliminate the fractions.

■ When simplifying expressions involving square roots you should

1. make the number under the square root sign as small as possible
2. rationalise the denominator.

EXERCISE 2.1 | Inequalities

LEVEL 1

1 Solve the following inequalities and represent their solution on a number line.

(i) $2x+3<11$

(ii) $12a+3 \leqslant 4a+5$

(iii) $\dfrac{x+3}{2} \geqslant 9$

(iv) $p-4>4p-13$

2 Solve the following inequalities and represent their solution on a number line.

(i) $3<4x+2<14$

(ii) $5 \geqslant 2x+3>0$

(iii) $\dfrac{4-2r}{3} \geqslant 6$

LEVEL 2

3 Solve the following inequalities and represent their solution on a number line.

(i) $7>1-3x>4$

(ii) $5>2+4x>1$

4 Write the following statements as a single inequality.

(i) $x>2$ and $3x<7$

(ii) $2x \leqslant 15$ and $3x \geqslant -2$

5 Solve the following inequalities either by drawing an appropriate quadratic graph or by factorising to reduce the inequality to two simultaneous linear inequalities.

(i) $x^2-3x+2<0$

(ii) $2a^2-7a-4 \leqslant 0$

(iii) $t^2-2t>3$

(iv) $(x-3)(x-5) \geqslant 8$

EXERCISE 2.2 | Algebraic fractions

LEVEL 1

1 Simplify the following.

(i) $\dfrac{6x+9}{(2x+3)(3x+2)}$

(ii) $\dfrac{2x^2y^3}{8xy^4}$

(iii) $\dfrac{a^2-4}{a^2+4a+4}$

2 Simplify the following.

(i) $\dfrac{2x}{3y} \times \dfrac{y^3}{5x^2}$

(ii) $\dfrac{x^2+3x+2}{2x-5} \times \dfrac{4x-10}{x^2+7x+10}$

(iii) $\dfrac{3p^2-12}{p^2+4p} \div \dfrac{p^2+5p+6}{p+4}$

3 Simplify the following.

(i) $\dfrac{5}{a^2} - \dfrac{2}{a}$ (ii) $\dfrac{4p}{3} + \dfrac{7p}{9}$ (iii) $\dfrac{3a}{2b} - \dfrac{2a}{3b}$

4 Simplify the following, giving the answer as a single fraction.

(i) $x - \dfrac{(2x)^2}{x^3} + 3x(-2x) + \dfrac{4}{x}$ (ii) $p^2 + \dfrac{2p}{(3p)^2} - \dfrac{4}{p} + 9p$

LEVEL 2

5 Simplify the following.

(i) $\dfrac{5x}{2x^2 + x} + \dfrac{4}{2x+1}$ (ii) $\dfrac{4a+2}{6a^2 + a - 1} - \dfrac{2a+1}{3a^2 + 5a - 2}$

6 Solve the following equations.

(i) $x + \dfrac{2x}{3} = 5$ (ii) $\dfrac{4}{p} - \dfrac{2}{3p} = \dfrac{2}{3}$ (iii) $\dfrac{3}{x} = \dfrac{7}{6} - \dfrac{1}{x+1}$

7 The numerator of a fraction is five less than the denominator. If the numerator and denominator are each increased by three, the value of the new fraction is $\frac{2}{3}$. Let x represent the denominator of the original fraction.

(i) Write down the original fraction in terms of x.

(ii) Write down the new fraction in terms of x.

(iii) Write down an equation and solve it to find x.

EXERCISE 2.3 # Simplifying expressions containing square roots

Do not use a calculator for this exercise.

LEVEL 1

1 Simplify the following as much as possible.

(i) $\sqrt{54}$ (ii) $\sqrt{8} \times \sqrt{2}$ (iii) $\sqrt{3}(3\sqrt{3} - 2)$

(iv) $\sqrt{8} + \sqrt{18} - 4\sqrt{2}$

2 Simplify the following as much as possible.

(i) $(\sqrt{5} + 6)(3 - \sqrt{5})$

(ii) $(3 + 2\sqrt{2})(2 - \sqrt{2})$

(iii) $(7 - \sqrt{3})^2$

3 Simplify the following by rationalising the denominators.

(i) $\dfrac{4}{\sqrt{2}}$ (ii) $\dfrac{\sqrt{27}}{\sqrt{6}}$ (iii) $\dfrac{1}{2\sqrt{2}}$

(iv) $\dfrac{5}{\sqrt{75}}$ (v) $\dfrac{5\sqrt{2}}{2\sqrt{5}}$

LEVEL 2

4 Solve the following equations, giving your answers as simply as possible in exact form.

(i) $x^2 - 4x + 1 = 0$

(ii) $4x^2 + 4x - 5 = 0$

(iii) $2x^2 - 2x - 1 = 0$

3

Algebra III – polynomials

Formulae you need to learn

- The factor theorem states that for any polynomial $f(x)$,
  $$f(a) = 0 \Leftrightarrow (x - a) \text{ is a factor of } f(x).$$
- The remainder theorem states that for any polynomial $f(x)$, if $f(x)$ is divided by $(x - a)$ then the remainder is $f(a)$.

KEY POINTS

- A polynomial in x has terms in positive integer powers of x, and may also have a constant term.

- The order of a polynomial in x is the highest power of x that appears in the polynomial.

Operations with polynomials

LEVEL 1

1 State the order of the following polynomials.

 (i) $5x^3 - 2x + 7$ **(ii)** $6 - 4x^5 + x^2$ **(iii)** $(2x - 3)^2$

2 **(i)** Add $6x^3 + 3x^2 - 2x - 7$ to $4x^2 - x - 9$.

 (ii) Subtract $3x^3 - 2x + 3$ from $x^4 + 2x^3 - x^2 + 1$.

 (iii) Simplify $(5x^3 - 2x + 3) - (2x - 5)^2$.

3 Multiply

 (i) $(2x^2 - 3x - 2)$ by $(3x - 1)$

 (ii) $(2x^4 - 3)$ by $(3x^2 + 5x - 1)$.

LEVEL 2

4 Simplify

 (i) $(x + 1)(x^2 - 1) - (x - 1)(x^2 + 1)$

 (ii) $(x - 1)^2(4x + 1) - (3x - 1)(x + 1)^2$.

5 Divide

 (i) $x^3 + 2x^2 - x - 2$ by $x - 1$

 (ii) $2x^3 + x + 18$ by $x + 2$.

The factor and remainder theorems

LEVEL 1

1 **(i)** Show that $x^3 - 2x^2 - 5x + 6$ is divisible by $(x - 1)$.

 (ii) Write $x^3 - 2x^2 - 5x + 6$ in the form $(x - 1)(x^2 + ax + b)$ where a and b are to be determined.

 (iii) Hence factorise $x^3 - 2x^2 - 5x + 6$ completely.

2 Find the value of a so that $f(x) = 2x^3 + 3x^2 - 7x + a$ is divisible by $(x + 2)$.

3 Find the remainder when $2x^3 + 3x - 2$ is divided by $(x + 2)$.

4 Use the factor theorem to factorise

(i) $x^3 - 3x^2 + 6x - 8$

(ii) $x^3 + 3x^2 + x + 3$

(iii) $2x^3 + 11x^2 + 17x + 6$.

5 (i) Divide $2x^3 + 13x^2 + 22x + 3$ by $(x + 3)$.

(ii) Hence show that $2x^3 + 13x^2 + 22x + 3 = 0$ has only one integer root.

6 Find the possible values of a if $(x - 2)$ is a factor of $x^3 + x^2 - 5ax + 2a^2$.

7 Find the possible values of a if the remainder when $3x^3 + ax^2 - 2a^2x + 5$ is divided by $(x + 1)$ is 3.

8 The polynomial $f(x) = x^3 + ax^2 + bx - 8$ has factors $(x - 1)$ and $(x + 2)$. Find the values of a and b and the other linear factor.

9 The polynomial $x^3 + ax^2 + bx + 6$ has factors $(x - 1)$ and $(x - 2)$. Find the values of a and b and the other linear factor.

10 The polynomial $x^3 + ax^2 + 5x + b$ has a factor of $(x - 1)$ and when it is divided by $(x + 2)$ the remainder is -48. Find the values of a and b.

11 Show that $x = 3$ is a root of the equation $2x^3 - 3x^2 - 11x + 6 = 0$ and hence solve the equation.

12 Which of the following three expressions have $(x + 2)$ as a factor?

(i) $x^3 - x^2 - 10x - 8$

(ii) $x^3 + x^2 - 8x + 12$

(iii) $2x^3 - x^2 - 10x$

LEVEL 3

13

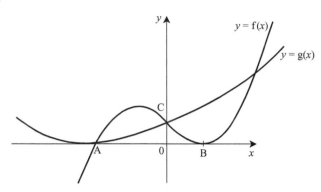

The diagram shows sketches of the graphs of $y = f(x)$ and $y = g(x)$ where $f(x) = x^3 + x^2 - 5x + 3$ and $g(x) = \dfrac{(x+3)^2}{3}$.

(i) Use the factor theorem to factorise $f(x)$.

(ii) Find the co-ordinates of the points A, B and C.

(iii) Find the co-ordinates of the other point of intersection of the two curves.

14 (i) Determine whether each of the following is a factor of the expression $x^3 - 19x + 30$. You must show your working.

    (a) $(x - 2)$ (b) $(x - 3)$

(ii) Factorise the expression $x^3 - 19x + 30$.

(iii) Solve the equation $x^3 - 19x + 30 = 0$.

15

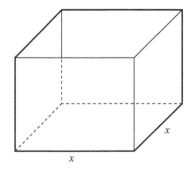

The diagram shows an open rectangular tank with a square base of side x metres and a volume of $18 \, \text{m}^3$.

(i) Write down an expression in terms of x for the height of the tank.

(ii) Show that the surface area of the tank is $\left(x^2 + \frac{72}{x}\right)m^2$.

(iii) Given that the surface area is $33\,m^2$, show that $x^3 - 33x + 72 = 0$.

(iv) Use the factor theorem to find a factor of $x^3 - 33x + 72 = 0$.

(v) Solve $x^3 - 33x + 72 = 0$ and hence find possible dimensions for the tank.

Algebra IV – applications

Formulae you need to learn

■ This formula for the binomial expansion is given on the formula sheet.

When n is a positive integer

$$(a+b)^n = a^n + \binom{n}{1}a^{n-1}b + \binom{n}{2}a^{n-2}b^2 + \ldots + \binom{n}{r}a^{n-r}b^r + \ldots + b^n$$

where $\binom{n}{r} = {}^nC_r = \dfrac{n!}{r!(n-r)!}$.

■ It is useful to remember how to draw Pascal's triangle.

The numbers in each line of the triangle give the binomial coefficients.

$$
\begin{array}{ccccccccccc}
 & & & & & 1 & & & & & \\
 & & & & 1 & & 1 & & & & \\
 & & & 1 & & 2 & & 1 & & & \\
 & & 1 & & 3 & & 3 & & 1 & & \\
 & 1 & & 4 & & 6 & & 4 & & 1 & \\
1 & & 5 & & 10 & & 10 & & 5 & & 1
\end{array}
$$

Each line begins and ends with 1, and each number in the triangle is the sum of the two numbers diagonally above it. You can see other patterns in the triangle. The triangle can be continued as far as you wish, but for large values of n it is better to use the formula.

■ The binomial coefficients, denoted by ${}^nC_r$ or $\binom{n}{r}$ can be found by using Pascal's triangle or the formula

$${}^nC_r = \dfrac{n!}{r!(n-r)!}.$$

■ The binomial expansion (given above) generalises to

$$(a+b)^n = {}^nC_0 a^n + {}^nC_1 a^{n-1}b + {}^nC_2 a^{n-2}b^2 + \ldots + {}^nC_n b^n.$$

■ The binomial distribution may be used to model a situation in which:

- the probability of a successful outcome is p

- the probability that the outcome is a failure is q where $q = 1 - p$

- there are n trials

- the number of successes is denoted by X.

Then $P(X = r) = {}^{n}C_{r}p^{r}q^{n-r}$ where $r = 0, 1, 2, ..., n$.

KEY POINTS

■ The following probability results will be useful:

- if a number of events are *independent* (i.e. the outcome of one does not affect the outcome of any other) then the probability that they all occur is found by multiplying the probabilities for each one.

- if two events are *mutually exclusive* (i.e. there is no overlap) then the probability of either one or the other occurring is the sum of the individual probabilities.

The binomial expansion

LEVEL 1

1 Write out these binomial expansions.

   (i) $(1+2x)^4$ **(ii)** $(1-3x)^3$ **(iii)** $(1+x^2)^5$

   (iv) $(x+3)^4$ **(v)** $(x+2y)^3$ **(vi)** $(2x-3y)^4$

2 Find the coefficient of x^3 in each of the following expansions.

   (i) $(1-2x)^6$ **(ii)** $(2x+3)^5$ **(iii)** $(1-2x)^{10}$

LEVEL 2

3 Simplify $(1+2x)^3-(1+x)^3$.

4 Expand $(1-3x)^3$ and use your result to expand $(2-x)(1-3x)^3$.

5 **(i)** Expand $(x+2)^3$.

   (ii) Find the values of x for which $(x+2)^3 = x^3+8$.

6 **(i)** Write down the first four terms in the expansion of $(1+2x)^6$.

   (ii) By choosing a suitable value of x find, without using a calculator, an approximate value for 1.02^6.

   (iii) Check 1.02^6 on your calculator and comment on the accuracy of your answer in **(ii)**.

LEVEL 3

7 **(i)** On the same axes for $0 \leqslant x \leqslant 1$ and $0 \leqslant y \leqslant 1$ plot the curves with equations

   (a) $y=1$ **(b)** $y=1-6x$

   (c) $y=1-6x+12x^2$ **(d)** $y=(1-2x)^3$.

   (ii) On your curves mark points A, B, C, D corresponding to the values of y when $x=0.2$.

   (iii) State the lengths on your graphs which represent the errors in estimating the value of 0.6^3 by using the following numbers of terms of the binomial expansion of $(1-2x)^3$.

   (a) 1   **(b)** 2   **(c)** 3

8

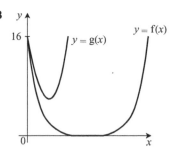

The diagram shows sketches of the graphs of $y = f(x)$ and $y = g(x)$ where $f(x) = (2-x)^4$ and $g(x)$ is a quadratic approximation to the curve obtained by using the first three terms in the binomial expansion of $f(x)$.

(i) Find $g(x)$ as a quadratic expression.

The curves clearly intersect at the point $(0, 16)$.

(ii) Do they intersect again, and if so where?

(iii) For what positive values of x would you suggest that the quadratic curve gives a good approximation to $y = f(x)$?

9 Many famous bridges, for example the Sydney Harbour Bridge, are in the shape of an arch.

One such bridge has an arch which is modelled by the curve $y = 0.4(16 - (x-2)^4)$ for $0 \leqslant x \leqslant 4$ as shown in the diagram below.

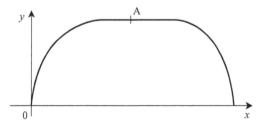

(i) (a) Write down the values of x when $16 - (x-2)^4 = 0$.

  (b) Hence write down the co-ordinates of the highest point A.

(ii) Show that $y = 0.4(32x - 24x^2 + 8x^3 - x^4)$.

(iii) If 1 unit represents 100 metres, calculate the minimum height of the bridge for the central 300 m.

The binomial distribution

LEVEL 1

1 (i) State the probability of throwing a 6 with a fair die.

(ii) Find the probability of throwing two consecutive 6s.

(iii) Find the probability of throwing at least two 6s in four throws.

2 It is believed that the proportion of drivers who fail a basic sight test is 1 in 6.

(i) Write down the probability that a driver chosen at random would pass the test.

(ii) Find the probability that in a sample of six drivers exactly half pass the test.

3 In a certain school, on average 15% of the pupils are learning to play a musical instrument. Find the probability that in a class of 30, 20% are learning to play a musical instrument.

LEVEL 2

4 At a particular dentist's surgery, records show that 10% of patients who make an appointment fail to turn up. There are 20 appointments one afternoon.

(i) Find the probability that all the patients turn up.

(ii) Find the probability that exactly 90% of the patients turn up.

(iii) Find the probability that at least 90% of the patients turn up.

5 A gardener buys a bag of 10 hyacinth bulbs in a sale. These have been in stock for some time, so he only expects 80% of them to flower.

(i) How many does he expect to flower?

(ii) What is the probability that more bulbs than he expects will flower?

6 The probability that a mug selected at random from a production line will be defective is on average 1 in 50. If more than 10% of any sample is defective the machine will be reset. In a sample of 20 mugs, find the probabilities that

(i) there are no defective mugs

(ii) the machine will need to be reset.

LEVEL 3

7 A bag contains six red and four black discs that are identical except for their colour. After each disc is chosen, its colour is noted, and then it is replaced. Five discs are chosen. Find

(i) the probability of choosing all red discs

(ii) the probability of choosing all discs of the same colour

(iii) the probability of choosing more red discs than black ones.

8 Alex is practising archery and on average is currently able to hit the target 2 out of 3 times. In order to secure a place on the team at the trials she needs to hit the target 9 times out of 10. What is the probability that she makes the team without improving her overall standard?

9 Martin likes rifle shooting at an amusement arcade and reckons he can hit the target 4 times out of 5 on average. Each 'go' consists of 10 independent shots and a prize is awarded for at least 9 'hits'.

(i) Show that the probability that Martin wins a prize in one 'go' is 0.376 correct to 3 significant figures.

(ii) Martin has two 'goes'. Giving your answers correct to 3 significant figures, find the probability that he wins

(a) exactly one prize

(b) at least one prize.

(iii) How many 'goes' does he need to have so that his probability of winning at least one prize is more than 90%?

10 Apples are sold in a supermarket in trays of eight. Due to problems in transit, some of the apples are slightly bruised when they arrive. For each apple, the probability that it is bruised is 0.02, independent of other apples. Find the probability that

(i) a tray contains no bruised apples

(ii) a tray contains exactly one bruised apple.

The manager initially decided that he cannot offer for sale trays which contain two or more bruised apples.

(iii) How many trays does he reject from a delivery of 1000 trays?

The manager then decides that it takes him too long to inspect all of the trays, so considers an alternative procedure. He samples five trays, and if two or more trays contain at least two bruised apples he rejects the whole delivery. If one tray contains at least two bruised apples, then he takes a further sample of five trays. If this sample also contains any trays with at least two bruised apples he then rejects the whole delivery.

(iv) What is the probability that he will reject the whole delivery?

SECTION 2
Co-ordinate geometry

Co-ordinate geometry I – straight lines and circles

Formulae you need to learn

- The gradient of the straight line joining the points (x_1, y_1) and (x_2, y_2) is given by gradient $= \dfrac{y_2 - y_1}{x_2 - x_1}$.
  The letter m is usually used to denote a gradient.

- If two lines have gradients m_1 and m_2, then:
  - they are parallel if $m_1 = m_2$
  - they are perpendicular if $m_1 m_2 = -1$.

- When the points A and B have co-ordinates (x_1, y_1) and (x_2, y_2) respectively then
  the distance AB $= \sqrt{(x_2 - x_1)^2 + (y_2 - y_1)^2}$ and the
  midpoint of AB has co-ordinates $\left(\dfrac{x_1 + x_2}{2}, \dfrac{y_1 + y_2}{2}\right)$.

- A sloping line through the origin with gradient m has equation $y = mx$.

- A sloping line through the point $(0, c)$ on the y axis with gradient m has equation $y = mx + c$.

- A line through the point (x_1, y_1) with gradient m has equation $(y - y_1) = m(x - x_1)$.

- A line parallel to the y axis, which passes through the point $(a, 0)$ on the x axis, has equation $x = a$. It has an infinitely large gradient.

- A line parallel to the x axis, which passes through the point $(0, b)$ on the y axis, has equation $y = b$. It has a zero gradient.

- The equation of a circle with centre (h, k) and radius r is $(x - h)^2 + (y - k)^2 = r^2$.

- When the centre is at the origin $(0, 0)$ this simplifies to $x^2 + y^2 = r^2$.

KEY POINTS

- A line parallel to the x axis is perpendicular to a line parallel to the y axis. You cannot use the relationship $m_1 m_2 = -1$ in this case.

- The co-ordinates of the point of intersection of two lines are found by solving their equations simultaneously.

Straight lines

LEVEL 1

1 A is the point $(-1, 3)$ and B is the point $(5, 11)$. Calculate

    (i) the gradient of the line AB

    (ii) the gradient of the line perpendicular to AB

    (iii) the length of AB

    (iv) the co-ordinates of the midpoint of AB.

2 The points A, B and C have co-ordinates $(-1, 4)$, $(2, 8)$ and $(6, 5)$ respectively.

    Show that the triangle ABC is isosceles.

3 Find the gradients of each of the following lines.

    (i) $3x - y = 0$ **(ii)** $x - 5y + 5 = 0$ **(iii)** $2x + 3y = 4$

LEVEL 2

4 For each of the following lines, find the equation of a parallel line passing through $(2, -4)$.

    (i) $y = 5x - 1$ **(ii)** $x + y = 2$ **(iii)** $3x - 2y = 1$

5 For each of the following lines, find the equation of a perpendicular line passing through $(-3, 1)$.

    (i) $y = 4x - 5$ **(ii)** $2x - y = 1$ **(iii)** $x + 4y = 0$

6 Find the equations of the lines through each of the following pairs of points.

    (i) $(0, 0)$ and $(5, -1)$

    (ii) $(1, -2)$ and $(3, -4)$

    (iii) $(3, -1)$ and $(2, 6)$

7 Sketch the following pairs of lines on the same axes and solve their equations simultaneously to find their point of intersection.

    (i) $y = 3x - 2$ **(ii)** $2x + 3y = 12$ **(iii)** $3x + y = 4$

         $x + y = 2$ $x - 2y = -1$ $5x - 2y = 3$

LEVEL 3

8 When the market price £p of an article sold on the free market varies, so does the number demanded D and the number supplied S. In one case $D = 20 + 0.1p$ and $S = p - 16$.

(i) Sketch both of these lines on the same graph. (Put p on the horizontal axis.)

The market reaches a state of equilibrium when the number demanded equals the number supplied.

(ii) Find the equilibrium price and the number bought and sold when the market is in equilibrium.

9 The line with equation $4x + 2y = 20$ meets the x axis at A and the line $y = x + 4$ meets the y axis at B. The two lines intersect at the point C.

(i) Sketch the two lines on the same diagram.

(ii) Calculate the co-ordinates of the points A, B and C.

(iii) Calculate the area of triangle OBC where O is the origin. 💡

(iv) Find the co-ordinates of the point D such that ABCD is a parallelogram.

EXERCISE 5.2   Circles

LEVEL 1

1 Find the equations of the following circles.

(i) centre (1, 1), radius 2

(ii) centre (2, 5), radius 3

(iii) centre (−1, −4), radius 5

2 For the circle $(x + 1)^2 + (y - 2)^2 = 4$

(i) state the radius and the co-ordinates of the centre of the circle

(ii) sketch the circle.

3 Show that the equation $x^2 + y^2 + 4x - 2y + 1 = 0$ represents a circle. Hence state the radius of the circle, give the co-ordinates of the centre and sketch the circle.

4 Determine whether the origin lies inside or outside the circle with equation $x^2 + y^2 - 6x + 8y = 11$. 💡

5 Both of the following pairs of equations give a line and a circle. In each case, determine whether the line intersects the circle, is a tangent to it or fails to meet it. You do not need to find the co-ordinates of any point of intersection.

(i) $x + y = 8$
$x^2 + y^2 = 25$

(ii) $2x + y = 5$
$(x - 4)^2 + (y - 2)^2 = 5$

6 (i) Sketch the circles $(x + 1)^2 + (y - 4)^2 = 9$ and $(x - 5)^2 + (y - 4)^2 = 16$ on the same axes and find their points of intersection.

(ii) What can you say about the relationship between the line joining their points of intersection and the line joining their centres?

(iii) Does this happen for every pair of intersecting circles?

6

Co-ordinate geometry II – applications

Formulae you need to learn

There are no formulae that you need to learn for this chapter.

- When illustrating linear inequalities:

  - represent boundaries for < and > as a *broken* line
  - represent boundaries for ≤ and ≥ as a *solid* line
  - specify the region that you want by shading out the *other* side of the line. This means that when you are illustrating a number of simultaneous inequalities, your final region will be left clear and uncluttered.

- The region where a number of inequalities are satisfied simultaneously is called the *feasible* region.

- In linear programming, the *objective function* is the algebraic expression describing the quantity that you are required to maximise or minimise.

- The maximum and minimum values of the objective function will lie at, or near, a vertex of the feasible region. If the answer to your problem requires the values to be integers, but the co-ordinates of the vertex of the feasible region are not in integers, then you need to search for an integer solution nearby which is inside the feasible region.

Drawing and using inequalities

You will need graph paper for this exercise.

LEVEL 1

1 On separate diagrams, use shading to denote each of the following inequalities.

(i) $x \geqslant 0$ **(ii)** $x+y<1$ **(iii)** $2x \leqslant 3y$

2 (i) Illustrate the feasible region for the following inequalities.

$x>2$

$y \geqslant 0$

$y \leqslant x$

$2x+3y<12$

(ii) Is the point (2, 1) in this feasible region?

LEVEL 2

3

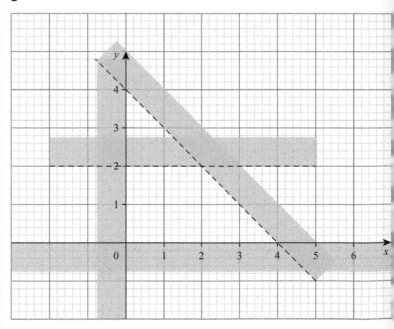

Write down the inequalities that define the region illustrated.

4 **(i)** Draw suitable graphs to maximise $C = x + y$
subject to

$2x + 3y \leqslant 12$

$3x + 2y \leqslant 15$

$x \geqslant 0$

$y \geqslant 0.$

(ii) Find the maximum value of C.

5 Solve the following problem graphically.
Maximise $2x + 3y$ subject to $x + y \leqslant 10$ and $2x + y \leqslant 14$.

LEVEL 3

6 A local school is putting on a concert in order to
raise money to sponsor a guide dog. The school hall
seats a maximum of 500 people and tickets are to be
priced at £8 each or £5 for children and concessions.
To encourage children to attend, it is decided that
at least one third of the tickets available should be
priced at £5.

(i) Using a to represent the number of £8 tickets and c
to represent the number of £5 tickets, write down all
inequalities that need to be satisfied, and illustrate
the region satisfied by these, using the horizontal
axis for a and the vertical axis for c.

(ii) Write down the objective function for the total
income £P and find the number of tickets in each
category which need to be sold to raise the greatest
amount of money.

(iii) Find the maximum income possible under these
constraints.

7 A toy company makes both dolls' prams and dolls'
pushchairs, which use the same wheels and logo
stickers. Each pram requires 4 wheels and 3 stickers,
and each pushchair requires 4 wheels and 2 stickers.
They have 2000 wheels and 1200 stickers available.

Using x to represent the number of prams and y to represent the number of pushchairs

(i) explain why $x+y \leqslant 500$ and find another similar inequality

(ii) draw a suitable diagram and shade it to indicate the feasible region.

Prams sell for £60 each and pushchairs for £50 each.

(iii) Write down the objective function for the total income £C from sales and add the direction of this line to your graph.

(iv) Find the number of each to maximise the income and hence find the maximum income available.

8 A local pottery is making two types of vases for sale.
Type A requires 1 hour of labour and costs £2 in raw materials.
Type B requires 2 hours of labour and costs £3 in raw materials.
From experience they know that the cheaper type of vase is more popular.
In any week there are 80 hours of labour available and up to £150 can be spent on raw materials for the vases.

Suppose that they make x of type A and y of type B per week.

(i) Explain why $x+2y \leqslant 80$ and find a similar inequality from the restriction on funds available.

(ii) Draw graphs of two lines and shade outside the feasible region.

The pottery makes a profit of £10 on type A and £18 on type B.

(iii) Write down the objective function.

(iv) Find the number of each that should be made to maximise the profit and hence find the maximum profit available.

9 A recipe for jam states that the weight of sugar used must be between the weight of fruit used and four-thirds of the weight of fruit used. Georgia has 10 kg of fruit available and 11 kg of sugar.

   (i) Using s kg to represent the weight of sugar and f kg to represent the weight of fruit, formulate inequalities to model this information.

   (ii) Draw a graph to represent your inequalities.

   (iii) Find the vertices of your feasible region and identify the points which would represent the best mix of ingredients under the following circumstances:

   (a) There is to be as much jam as possible, given that the weight of jam produced is the sum of the weights of the fruit and the sugar.

   (b) There is to be as much jam as possible given that it is to have the lowest possible proportion of sugar.

   (c) There is to be as much jam as possible given that it is to have the highest possible proportion of sugar.

   (d) Fruit costs £2 per kg, sugar costs £1 per kg and the objective is to produce as much jam as possible within a budget of £15.

   [MEI (*amended*)]

10 A haulage company has to transport 2000 packages using a combination of large vans which can take 300 packages each and small vans which can take 100 packages each. The cost of running each large van is £200 and the cost of running each small van is £100. The total cost must not exceed £1800. How can this be achieved minimising the cost?

SECTION 3
Trigonometry

Trigonometry I – review

Formulae you need to learn

- For an angle θ in a right-angled triangle

$$\sin\theta = \frac{\text{opposite}}{\text{hypotenuse}}, \cos\theta = \frac{\text{adjacent}}{\text{hypotenuse}}, \tan\theta = \frac{\text{opposite}}{\text{adjacent}}.$$

- $\tan\theta = \dfrac{\sin\theta}{\cos\theta}$

- $\sin^2\theta + \cos^2\theta = 1$
- For a triangle ABC

  - area $= \frac{1}{2}bc\sin A$

  - the sine rule has two forms:

    $\dfrac{a}{\sin A} = \dfrac{b}{\sin B} = \dfrac{c}{\sin C}$ which is used to find a side, and

    $\dfrac{\sin A}{a} = \dfrac{\sin B}{b} = \dfrac{\sin C}{c}$ which is used to find an angle

  - the alternative form of the cosine rule, not given on the formula sheet, is $\cos A = \dfrac{b^2 + c^2 - a^2}{2bc}$.

- The formula for the cosine rule given on the formula sheet is $a^2 = b^2 + c^2 - 2bc\cos A$.

KEY POINTS

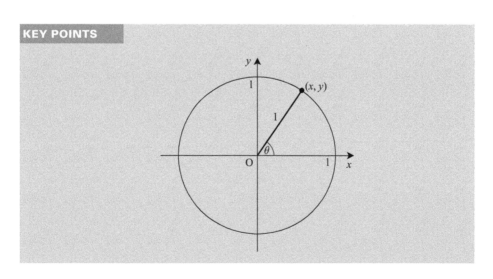

- The point (x, y) at angle θ on the unit circle with centre $(0, 0)$ has co-ordinates $(\cos \theta, \sin \theta)$ for all values of θ, i.e. $\cos \theta = x$ and $\sin \theta = y$. This also gives $\tan \theta = \frac{y}{x}$, i.e. $\tan \theta = \frac{\sin \theta}{\cos \theta}$.

- The graphs of $\sin \theta$, $\cos \theta$ and $\tan \theta$ are shown below:

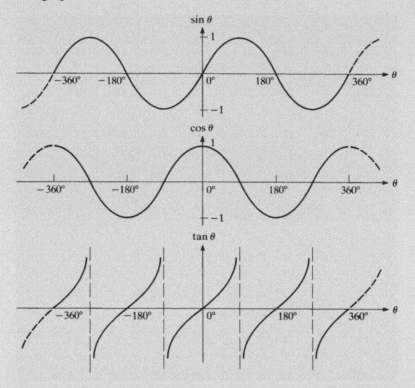

Notice that whatever the size of the angle, $\sin \theta$ and $\cos \theta$ can only ever take values between –1 and +1, but $\tan \theta$ can take all positive and negative values.

The dashed lines parallel to the y axis on the $\tan \theta$ graph are called *asymptotes* and indicate values of θ for which there is no value of $\tan \theta$.

The trigonometrical ratios

LEVEL 1

1 Find the length marked x in each of these triangles. Give your answers correct to 1 decimal place.

(i)

7 cm, 18°

(ii)

51°, x, 2.8 cm

2 Find the angle marked θ in each of these triangles. Give your answers correct to 1 decimal place.

(i) 4 cm

9 cm, θ

(ii) 10.2 cm

θ, 6.9 cm

LEVEL 2

3 Two points A and B are 200 m apart and the bearing of B from A is 153°.

(i) How far is B south of A?

(ii) How far is B east of A?

Give your answers to the nearest metre.

4 Solve the following equations for $0° \leqslant \theta \leqslant 360°$, giving your answers to 1 decimal place where necessary.

(i) $\sin\theta = 0.2$ **(ii)** $\cos\theta = \frac{\sqrt{3}}{2}$ **(iii)** $\tan\theta = 4$

(iv) $\sin\theta = -0.7$ **(v)** $\cos\theta = -0.9$ **(vi)** $\tan\theta = -1$

5 Solve the following equations for $0° \leqslant \theta \leqslant 360°$, giving your answers correct to 1 decimal place.

(i) $2 + 3\sin\theta = 1$ **(ii)** $4\cos\theta - 2 = 1$

6 For the following questions, give your answers correct to 1 decimal place.

(i) Find 2θ if $\cos 2\theta = 0.4$ for $0° \leqslant 2\theta \leqslant 360°$.

(ii) Hence find values of θ so that $\cos 2\theta = 0.4$ for $0° \leqslant \theta \leqslant 180°$.

7 Solve $\tan 2\theta = 2$ for $0° \leqslant \theta \leqslant 180°$, giving your answers correct to 1 decimal place.

LEVEL 3

8 Solve $\tan^2\theta + 3\tan\theta - 4 = 0$ for $-180° \leqslant \theta \leqslant 180°$, giving your answers correct to 1 decimal place.

EXERCISE 7.2 # The trigonometrical identities

LEVEL 2

1 (i) Use the identity $\tan\theta = \dfrac{\sin\theta}{\cos\theta}$ to rewrite the equation $2\sin\theta = \cos\theta$ in terms of $\tan\theta$.

(ii) Hence solve the equation $2\sin\theta = \cos\theta$ for $-180° \leqslant \theta \leqslant 180°$, giving your answers correct to 1 decimal place.

2 (i) Use the identity $\sin^2\theta + \cos^2\theta = 1$ to rewrite the equation $\sin^2\theta = 2\cos^2\theta - 1$ in terms of $\cos\theta$.

(ii) Hence solve the equation $\sin^2\theta = 2\cos^2\theta - 1$ for $0° \leqslant \theta \leqslant 360°$, giving your answers correct to 1 decimal place.

3 Solve $\sin^2 x = 1$ for $-360° \leqslant x \leqslant 360°$.

4 The diagram shows part of the curves $y = \sin x$ and $y = 2\cos x$ which intersect at A.

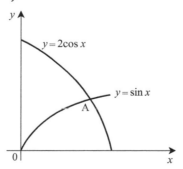

Find the co-ordinates of A.

LEVEL 3

5 Solve $2\sin^2 x = 5\cos x + 4$ for $0° \leqslant x \leqslant 360°$.

6 Solve $\sin^2 x = 2\cos^2 x$ for $0° \leqslant x \leqslant 360°$, giving your answers correct to 1 decimal place.

EXERCISE 7.3 ## The sine and cosine rules and area of a triangle formula

LEVEL 1

1 Find the length x in each of the following triangles, giving your answer correct to 1 decimal place.

(i)   (ii)

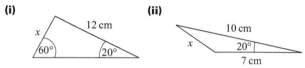

2 Find the angle θ in each of the following triangles, giving your answer correct to 1 decimal place.

(i)   (ii)

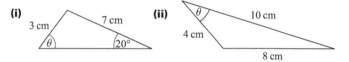

3 Find the area of each of the following triangles, giving your answer correct to 1 decimal place.

(i)   (ii)

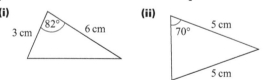

LEVEL 2

4

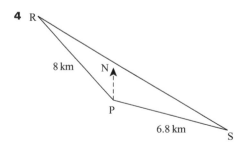

From a port P, two ships R and S are on bearings of 315° and 092° respectively. The distance PR = 8 km and the distance PS = 6.8 km. Find the distance between the ships, giving your answer correct to 1 decimal place.

5 A vertical tower CD stands with its base C on horizontal ground. The angle of elevation of the top of the tower from a point A on the ground is 12° and, from a point B in line with A and C, and with AB = 100 m, the angle of elevation is 25°. Giving your answers correct to 1 decimal place, calculate

(i) ∠ADB

(ii) AD

(iii) the height of the tower.

6 Two adjacent sides of a parallelogram are of lengths 10.3 cm and 7.2 cm respectively, and the angle between them is 52°.

(i) Find the lengths of the diagonals of the parallelogram, giving your answers correct to 1 decimal place.

(ii) Find the area of the parallelogram correct to 1 decimal place.

7 The diagram shows a village green bordered by three straight roads. The road PQ runs due north.

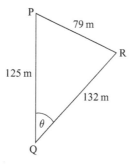

Find

(i) the bearing of R from Q to the nearest degree

(ii) the area of the village green to the nearest square metre.

LEVEL 3

8

A tower 85 m high stands on the top of a hill. From a point on the ground at sea level, the angles of elevation of the top and the bottom of the tower are 45° and 25° respectively. Find the height of the hill to the nearest metre. 💡

9 A walker at point A can see the spires of St. Benedict's (B) and St. Cuthbert's (C) on bearings of 330° and 037° respectively. He then walks 400 m due north to a point D, from which the bearings are 310° and 084° respectively. Assume that all measurements are exact and that they are made in the same horizontal plane.

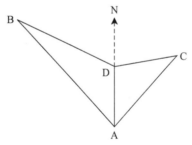

(i) Copy the diagram and add all the information from the question.

(ii) Calculate the distance AB to the nearest metre.

(iii) Given that the distance AC is 567 m, calculate BC, the distance between the spires, to the nearest metre.

10 At 12:00 a.m. the Captain of a ship observes that the bearing of a lighthouse L is 340°. His position is at A. At 12:30 a.m. he takes another bearing of the lighthouse and finds it to be 030°. During this time the ship moves on a constant course of 280° to the point B.

His plot on the chart is shown below.

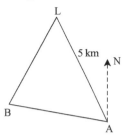

(i) Write down the size of the angles ∠LAB and ∠LBA.

(ii) The Captain believes that at A he is 5 km from L. Assuming that LA is exactly 5 km, show that LB is 4.61 km, correct to 2 decimal places, and find AB, also correct to 2 decimal places.

(iii) Hence calculate the speed of the ship to 1 decimal place.

[MEI (*amended*)]

8 Trigonometry II – applications

Formulae you need to learn

There are no formulae that you need to learn for this chapter.

- In three dimensions:
  - a plane is a flat surface
  - the line of greatest slope of a plane is the steepest line contained in the plane
  - two lines may meet, be parallel or be skew
  - two planes are either parallel or meet in a line
  - a line and a plane may be parallel, meet in a single point or the line may lie in the plane.

- When solving three-dimensional problems always draw a clear diagram where:
  - vertical lines are drawn vertically
  - east–west lines are drawn horizontally
  - north–south lines are drawn sloping
  - edges that are hidden are drawn as dotted lines.

Trigonometry–applications to 3-D

LEVEL 2

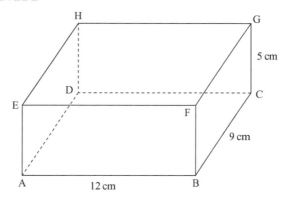

1   The jewellery box shown in the diagram is in the shape
    of a cuboid with sides of length 12 cm, 9 cm and 5 cm.

    (i)   Find the length AC.

    (ii) Find the angle that AG makes with the base ABCD.

    (iii) Find the length AF.

    (iv) Find the angle that AG makes with the front ABFE.

2

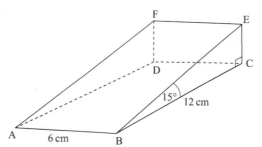

A door wedge is in the shape of a prism, with
dimensions as shown in the diagram.

(i)   Find the length CE.

(ii) Find the volume of wood in the wedge.

(iii) What is the maximum number of such wedges that
       can be made from a block of wood 10 cm by 30 cm
       by 2 m? 💡

3

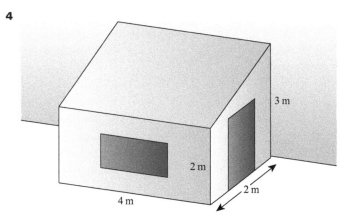

A perfume bottle is made in the shape of a square-based pyramid with the vertex directly above the centre of the base, and has dimensions as shown in the diagram.

(i) Find the angle between a slant edge and the base.

(ii) Find the angle between a side and the base.

4

The diagram shows a lean-to shed which is used to store garden equipment and materials. The base of the shed is 2 m by 4 m and the height is 2 m at the front and 3 m at the back.

(i) Find the angle of inclination of the roof to the horizontal.

(ii) Find the volume of the shed.

The door is 80 cm wide and 2 m high and is positioned in the middle of the end wall.

(iii) Find the length of the longest metal rod that can be stored in the shed. 💡

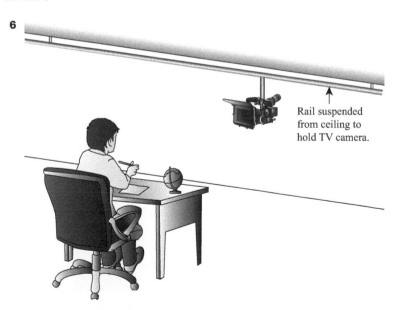

Mollie's route

James' route

15°

Mollie is an advanced skier who is able to ski straight down a 100 m run on a slope inclined at 15° to the horizontal. James is a novice who can only ski slopes inclined at 5°, so needs to go across the slope as indicated in the diagram.

By considering the ski slope as a wedge, find

(i) the vertical fall of the 100 m run

(ii) the distance skied by James in getting from the top to the bottom, assuming James skies in a straight line across the slope.

LEVEL 3

6

Rail suspended from ceiling to hold TV camera.

Jon is presenting the news on television while seated at his desk in the studio. The TV camera runs on a horizontal track which is suspended from the ceiling and the camera is at a height of 2.2 m above the floor and 3 m horizontally away from Jon. The camera track is 4 m long and Jon is seated opposite the centre of the track. Jon's eye level when seated is 1.25 m above the floor. Giving distances to 2 decimal places and angles to 1 decimal place,

(i) find the least and greatest distances between Jon's eyes and the camera

(ii) find the range of angles between Jon's line of sight and the horizontal, assuming that he is looking directly at the camera.

7

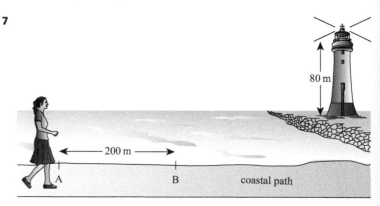

Nina is walking along a straight coastal path at sea level, and is at the point A in the diagram, when she notices that the angle of inclination of the top of the lighthouse is 5°. After walking a further 200 m she reaches the point B and notices that the angle of elevation is now 6°. The top of the lighthouse is 80 m above sea level. Giving all answers to the nearest metre,

(i) find the distances from each of the points A and B to the foot of the lighthouse.

By first calculating suitable angles, calculate

(ii) how much further she needs to walk before she is directly opposite the base of the lighthouse

(iii) how far the base of the lighthouse is from the coastal path.

SECTION 4
Calculus

9

Calculus I – differentiation

Formulae you need to learn

- $y = c \Rightarrow \dfrac{\mathrm{d}y}{\mathrm{d}x} = 0$ where c is a constant.

- $y = x^n \Rightarrow \dfrac{\mathrm{d}y}{\mathrm{d}x} = nx^{n-1}$ where n is a positive integer.

- $y = kx^n \Rightarrow \dfrac{\mathrm{d}y}{\mathrm{d}x} = knx^{n-1}$ where n is a positive integer and k is constant.

KEY POINTS

- Sometimes the notation $\mathrm{f}(x)$ will be used instead of y. In that case the notation $\mathrm{f}'(x)$ will replace $\dfrac{\mathrm{d}y}{\mathrm{d}x}$.

- $y = \mathrm{f}(x) + \mathrm{g}(x) + c \Rightarrow \dfrac{\mathrm{d}y}{\mathrm{d}x} = \mathrm{f}'(x) + \mathrm{g}'(x)$

  For example
  $y = 2x^2 + 3x - 7 \Rightarrow \dfrac{\mathrm{d}y}{\mathrm{d}x} = 4x + 3.$

- Remove all brackets before differentiating.

  For example
  $y = (x - 3)(x + 2)$
  $\quad = x^2 - x - 6$
  $\Rightarrow \dfrac{\mathrm{d}y}{\mathrm{d}x} = 2x - 1.$

- For the tangent and normal at (x_1, y_1)

  - the gradient of the tangent, $m_1 =$ the value of $\dfrac{dy}{dx}$ at (x_1, y_1)

  - the gradient of the normal, $m_2 = -\dfrac{1}{m_1}$

  - the equation of the tangent is $(y - y_1) = m_1(x - x_1)$

  - the equation of the normal is $(y - y_1) = m_2(x - x_1)$.

- At a stationary point, $\dfrac{dy}{dx} = 0$.

  The nature of the stationary point can be determined by looking at the sign of the gradient either side of it.

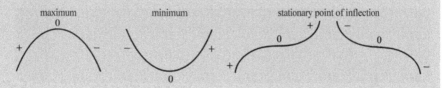

Introducing differentiation

LEVEL 1

1 Differentiate the following functions.

(i) $y = x^5$ (ii) $y = 3x^7$

(iii) $y = 4$ (iv) $y = 2x^9 - 3x^2$

(v) $y = \frac{3}{2}x^6 + 2x + 1$ (vi) $y = 5 - \frac{x^3}{3}$

(vii) $v = 2t^3 + 3$ (viii) $V = \frac{4}{3}\pi r^3$

(ix) $s = 2t^2 - 4t + 1$ (x) $y = (2x+3)(x+1)$

(xi) $y = (x^2+1)(x-1)$ (xii) $y = (4x+1)^2$

2 The gradient of the curve $y = x^4 + kx^2 + 3$ at the point where $x = -1$ is -8. Find the value of k.

3 The function f(x) is defined by f(x) = $(x-1)(x^2+2)$.

(i) Find f'(x).

(ii) Find f'(-2).

LEVEL 2

4

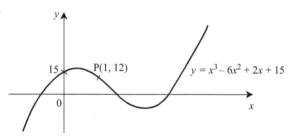

The sketch shows the point P(1, 12) on the graph of $y = x^3 - 6x^2 + 2x + 15$. Find

(i) the gradient function $\dfrac{dy}{dx}$

(ii) the gradient of the curve at the point P

(iii) the equation of the tangent to the curve at the point P

(iv) the equation of the normal at the point P.

5

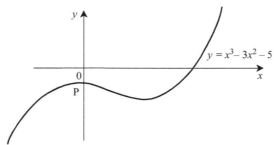

The sketch shows the point P(–1, –8) on the graph of $y = 9x - x^3$. Find

(i) the gradient function $\dfrac{dy}{dx}$

(ii) the gradient of the curve at the point P

(iii) the equation of the tangent to the curve at the point P

(iv) the equation of the normal at the point P.

6

The sketch shows the graph of $y = x^3 - 3x^2 - 5$. Find

(i) the gradient function $\dfrac{dy}{dx}$

(ii) the gradient of the curve at the point P where it crosses the y axis

(iii) the equation of the tangent to the curve at the point P

(iv) the equation of the normal to the curve at the point P.

7

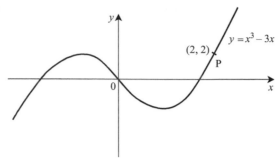

The sketch shows the graph of $y = x^3 - 3x$.

(i) Find the equation of the tangent to the curve at the point P(2, 2).

(ii) Verify that the tangent meets the curve again at the point where $x = -4$.

(iii) Find the value of y at this point of intersection.

8

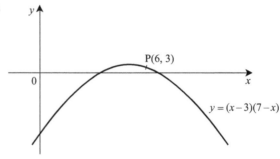

The sketch shows the graph of $y = (x - 3)(7 - x)$.

(i) Find the equation of the tangent to the curve at the point P(6, 3).

(ii) Find the equation of the normal to the curve at P.

(iii) Verify that the normal passes through the origin.

9 A cubic curve has equation $y = x(x - 2)(x - 3)$.

(i) Find $\dfrac{dy}{dx}$.

(ii) Find the gradient of the curve at each of the points where it crosses the x axis.

10

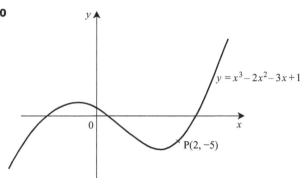

The sketch shows the graph of $y = x^3 - 2x^2 - 3x + 1$.

(i) Find the equation of the tangent at the point P(2, –5).

(ii) Find the co-ordinates of the point where this tangent meets the curve again.

11

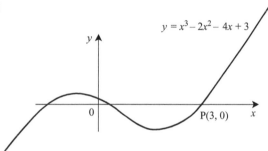

The sketch shows the graph of $y = x^3 - 2x^2 - 4x + 3$. Find

(i) the equation of the tangent at the point P(3, 0)

(ii) the x co-ordinate of another point Q on the curve where the tangent at Q is parallel to the tangent at P.

12

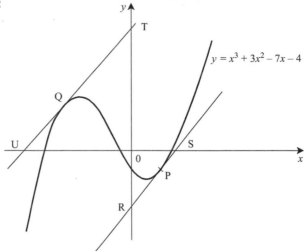

The sketch shows the graph of $y = x^3 + 3x^2 - 7x - 4$. Find

(i) $\dfrac{dy}{dx}$

(ii) the co-ordinates of the points P and Q, given that the gradient of the tangent to the curve is 2 at both points

(iii) the equations of these two tangents.

The tangent at P intersects the co-ordinate axes at R and S and the tangent at Q intersects them at T and U.

(iv) Find the area of the quadrilateral RSTU.

(v) What special type of quadrilateral is this?

EXERCISE 9.2 # Stationary points

LEVEL 2

1 For each of the curves given below:

(a) find $\dfrac{dy}{dx}$ and the value(s) of x for which $\dfrac{dy}{dx} = 0$

(b) classify the point(s) on the curve with these x values

(c) find the corresponding y values

(d) sketch the curve.

(i) $y = x^3 - 6x^2 + 4$

(ii) $y = x^4 - 8x^2 + 16$

(iii) $y = 9x + 3x^2 - x^3$

(iv) $y = x^4 - 4x^3 + 6$

2 A curve has equation $y = x^3 - 2x^2 - 4x + 3$.

    (i) Find the co-ordinates of the stationary points and distinguish between them.

    (ii) Sketch the curve.

3 A curve has equation $y = 3x^3 + ax^2 + bx + 4$ and when $x = 1$, $y = 5$ and $\dfrac{dy}{dx} = 2$.

    (i) Using the information given, write down two equations involving a and b and solve them simultaneously.

    (ii) Show that the curve has no stationary points.

4 Find the position and nature of the stationary points of the curve $f(x) = x^3 + 2x^2 - 4x + 3$.

5 The graph of $y = x^3 - 3x^2 + px + q$, where p and q are constants, passes through the point $(2, -12)$ and its gradient at that point is -9.

    (i) Find the values of p and q.

    (ii) Find the co-ordinates of the stationary points of the function and distinguish between them.

    (iii) Sketch the curve.

6 A function is said to be 'increasing' when $\dfrac{dy}{dx} > 0$ and 'decreasing' when $\dfrac{dy}{dx} < 0$. For the function $f(x) = x^3 - 3x + 4$

    (i) locate and classify the turning points of the curve

    (ii) sketch the curve

    (iii) determine the ranges of values of x for which $f(x)$ is an increasing function

    (iv) determine the range of values of x for which $f(x)$ is a decreasing function.

7 The curve $y = ax^3 - 3x + 2b$ has a turning point at the point with co-ordinates (a, b) where $a > 0$.

  (i) Use the fact that (a, b) is on the curve to write down a first equation connecting a and b.

  (ii) Use the fact that (a, b) is a turning point to write down a second equation.

  (iii) Solve these equations to find a and b.

  (iv) Prove that (a, b) is a minimum turning point.

8 The curve $y = a + bx^3 + cx^4$ has a maximum turning point at $(-2, 20)$ and a point of inflexion at $(0, 4)$.

  (i) Use the fact that these points are on the curve to write down two equations connecting a, b and c.

  (ii) Use other information given in the question to write down a further equation connecting a, b and c.

  (iii) Solve these equations to find values for a, b and c.

  (iv) Sketch the curve.

9

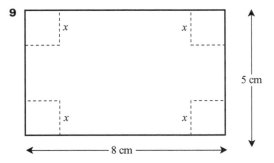

The diagram shows a rectangular sheet of cardboard 8 cm by 5 cm. Equal squares of side x cm are cut from each corner and the edges are then turned up to make an open box. Denoting the volume of the box by V cm³, show that $V = 4x^3 - 26x^2 + 40x$. Find the only viable stationary point and prove that it is a maximum.

10 Calculus II – integration

Formulae you need to learn

- $\dfrac{dy}{dx} = x^n \Rightarrow y = \dfrac{x^{n+1}}{n+1} + c$ c is constant

- $\dfrac{dy}{dx} = k \Rightarrow y = kx + c$ k and c are constants

- $\displaystyle\int_a^b x^n \, dx = \left[\dfrac{x^{n+1}}{n+1}\right]_a^b = \dfrac{b^{n+1} - a^{n+1}}{n+1}$ Notice no $+c$ here

- $\displaystyle\int_a^b k \, dx = [kx]_a^b = kb - ka$ k is a constant

For example $\displaystyle\int_1^2 x^3 \, dx = \left[\dfrac{x^4}{4}\right]_1^2 = \dfrac{2^4 - 1^4}{4} = \dfrac{15}{4}$.

KEY POINTS

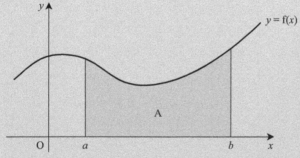

Area $A = \displaystyle\int_a^b y \, dx = \int_a^b f(x) \, dx$

- Areas below the x axis give rise to negative values for the integral.

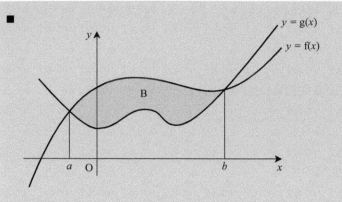

$$\text{Area B} = \int\limits_{a}^{b} \left(\text{top curve} - \text{bottom curve}\right) dx = \int\limits_{a}^{b}(f(x) - g(x))\, dx$$

Introduction to integration

LEVEL 1

1 For each of the gradient functions find $y = f(x)$.

(i) $\dfrac{dy}{dx} = 4x - 2$

(ii) $\dfrac{dy}{dx} = 3x^2 + 2x - 1$

(iii) $\dfrac{dy}{dx} = 5$

(iv) $f'(x) = x^3 - 3x^2 + 1$

(v) $f'(x) = (x - 2)^2$

(vi) $f'(x) = 4 - 2x$

2 Find the following indefinite integrals.

(i) $\displaystyle\int 3x^2 \, dx$

(ii) $\displaystyle\int (2x^4 - 3x^2 + 4) \, dx$

(iii) $\displaystyle\int (x + 1)(x - 1) \, dx$

(iv) $\displaystyle\int (5 + 2x) \, dx$

(v) $\displaystyle\int (x - 1)^2 \, dx$

(vi) $\displaystyle\int 4 \, dx$

LEVEL 2

3 For each of the following gradient functions find the equation of the curve $y = f(x)$ that passes through the given point.

(i) $\dfrac{dy}{dx} = 2x + 4;\ (2, 7)$

(ii) $\dfrac{dy}{dx} = x^2 + 1;\ (-3, 4)$

(iii) $f'(x) = (x + 1)^2;\ (2, 3)$

(iv) $f'(x)(x) = (x - 1)(x + 1);\ (3, 2)$

4 You are given that $\dfrac{dy}{dx} = 4x - 3$.

(i) Find the general solution of the differential equation.

(ii) Find the particular solution that passes through $(-1, 5)$.

LEVEL 3

5 The curve C passes through $(4, -2)$ and its gradient function is given by $f'(x) = 3x^2 - 6x - 4$.

(i) Find the equation of the curve.

(ii) Find the co-ordinates of the points where the curve intersects the line $y = -2$.

6 The gradient function of a curve is $6x^2 - 6$. The curve has two stationary points, one a maximum with a y value of 7 and the other a minimum with a y value of -1.

(i) Find the value of x at each stationary point.

(ii) Find the equation of the curve.

(iii) Sketch the curve.

7 The curve with gradient function $3x^2 - 2x - 1$ passes through the point $(2, 3)$.

(i) Find the equation of the curve.

(ii) Find the co-ordinates of any stationary points for the curve.

(iii) Sketch the curve.

EXERCISE 10.2 **Definite integrals and areas**

LEVEL 1

1 Evaluate

(i) $\left[\dfrac{x^3}{3}\right]_1^2$ (ii) $\left[3x^2 + 2x\right]_0^3$ (iii) $\left[x^3 + 2x\right]_{-2}^2$.

2 Evaluate the following definite integrals.

(i) $\displaystyle\int_0^2 4x\,dx$ (ii) $\displaystyle\int_{-3}^3 x^2\,dx$ (iii) $\displaystyle\int_{-2}^4 (2x+5)\,dx$

(iv) $\displaystyle\int_{-3}^3 (9-x^2)\,dx$ (v) $\displaystyle\int_{-1}^1 (x+1)(x-1)\,dx$

(vi) $\displaystyle\int_0^3 (3x^2 - 2x + 9)\,dx$

LEVEL 2

3 Find the area of each shaded region in the sketches that follow.

(i)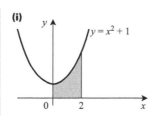

(ii)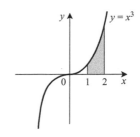

(iii)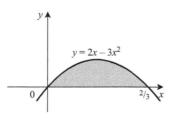

(iv)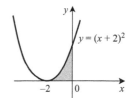

4

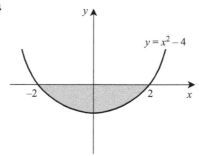

The sketch shows part of the curve $y = x^2 - 4$.

Calculate the area of the shaded region.

5

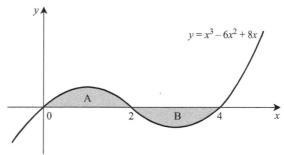

The sketch shows the curve $y = x^3 - 6x^2 + 8x$.

(i) Calculate each of the shaded areas A and B.

(ii) Evaluate $\displaystyle\int_0^4 (x^3 - 6x^2 + 8x)\, dx$.

(iii) What do you notice?

LEVEL 3

6 (i) Sketch the curve $y = x^2 - 3x$ for $-1 \leqslant x \leqslant 4$.

(ii) For what values of x does the curve lie below the x axis?

(iii) Find the area between the curve and the x axis.

7 (i) Shade, on a suitable sketch, the region whose area is given by $\displaystyle\int_{-1}^{3} (4+x)(4-x)\,dx$.

(ii) Find the area of the shaded region.

8

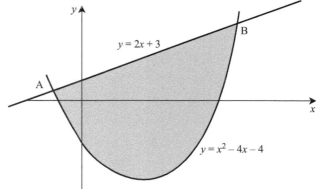

The sketch shows the graphs of the curve $y = x^2 - 4x - 4$ and the line $y = 2x + 3$ which intersect at the points A and B.

(i) Find the co-ordinates of A and B.

(ii) Find the area of the shaded region.

9

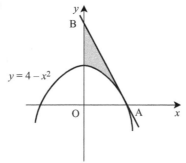

The sketch shows the graph of $y = 4 - x^2$ and the tangent to the curve at the point A(2, 0).

(i) Find the equation of the tangent AB.

(ii) Find the area of the shaded region.

10

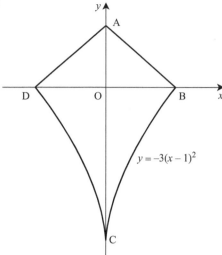

$$y = -3(x - 1)^2$$

A kite ABCD is constructed using the pattern in the diagram, where the y axis is a line of symmetry and AO = OB.

(i) Find the equation of the line AB.

(ii) Find the area of ABCD. 💡

(iii) Find the area of the kite if 1 unit represents 40 cm.

11

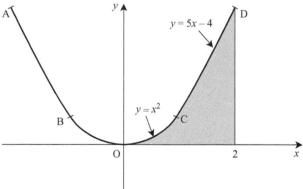

$y = 5x - 4$

$y = x^2$

A drainage ditch is being dug with a symmetrical cross-section ABCD as shown in the diagram. The equation of OC is $y = x^2$ and the equation of CD is $y = 5x - 4$.

(i) Find the area of the shaded region.

(ii) Find the volume of earth removed in a 100 m length of ditch if 1 unit represents 50 cm.

Calculus III – applications to kinematics

Formulae you need to learn

- When the acceleration, a, is constant, the initial velocity is u, and at time t the velocity is v and the displacement is s:

  - $v = u + at$
  - $s = \dfrac{u+v}{2}t$
  - $s = ut + \tfrac{1}{2}at^2$
  - $v^2 = u^2 + 2as$.

- For general motion
  - $v = \dfrac{ds}{dt}$ (Velocity is the gradient of a displacement–time graph.)
  - $a = \dfrac{dv}{dt}$ (Acceleration is the gradient of a velocity–time graph.)
  - $s = \int v\, dt$ (Displacement is the area under a velocity–time graph.)
  - $v = \int a\, dt$.   (Velocity is the area under an acceleration–time graph.)

Quantity	Definition	S.I. unit	Symbol	Notation
Time	Measured from a fixed origin	second	s	t
Distance	Distance travelled in a given time	metre	m	x (or y)
Speed	Rate of change of distance	metre per second	ms^{-1}	$v = \dfrac{dx}{dt}$
Displacement	Distance from a fixed origin	metre	m	s (or h)
Velocity	Rate of change of displacement	metre per second	ms^{-1}	$v = \dfrac{ds}{dt}$
Acceleration	Rate of change of velocity	metre per second per second	ms^{-2}	$a = \dfrac{dv}{dt}$

■ Motion under gravity, with no air resistance, is subject to an acceleration of g. The value of g is about 9.8 ms–2 on Earth.

■ When an object is dropped, its initial velocity is zero.

■ When an object travels upwards, its velocity is zero when it reaches its maximum height and

■ when an object returns to its initial position its displacement is 0.

Motion with constant acceleration

Throughout this exercise take the acceleration due to gravity as $9.8\,ms^{-2}$ unless instructed otherwise.

LEVEL 1

1 Decide which *suvat* equation to use in each of these situations.

(i) Given a, u, v find t.

(ii) Given a, s, v find u.

(iii) Given s, t, u find a.

(iv) Given t, u, v find s.

2 (i) Find s when $u=0$, $v=5$, $t=2$.

(ii) Find t when $u=2$, $v=7$, $a=0.4$.

(iii) Find a when $u=-2$, $v=4$, $s=3$.

(iv) Find v when $u=3$, $a=-2$, $t=3$ and interpret the result.

(v) Find u when $s=10$, $a=3$, $t=4$ and interpret the result.

LEVEL 2

3 A stone is dropped from a height of 8 m.

(i) How long does it take to reach the ground?

(ii) How fast is it moving when it reaches the ground?

4 A ball is thrown vertically upwards from a point A with a speed of $12\,ms^{-1}$ and later caught at the same point A. Find the length of time for which the ball is in the air.

5 What acceleration, in ms^{-2}, is needed to increase the speed of a car from rest to $5\,ms^{-1}$ in 4 seconds?

6 A car accelerates uniformly from a speed of $36\,km\,h^{-1}$ to a speed of $81\,km\,h^{-1}$ in 10 seconds as it travels along a straight road.

(i) Calculate the acceleration of the car in ms^{-2}.

(ii) Calculate the distance travelled in that time, giving your answer to the nearest metre.

7 A firework rises vertically from the ground to a height of 100 m in 5 s. Assuming that the firework starts from rest and has a constant acceleration,

(i) find its speed when it reaches a height of 100 m.

After 5 s the firework burns out and continues to move vertically under gravity.

(ii) Find the maximum height reached by the firework.

(iii) Find the total time that the firework is in the air.

8 An object moves along a straight line. It starts at the origin with a velocity of 8 ms^{-1} and has a constant acceleration of -5 ms^{-2}.

(i) After how long is the object instantaneously at rest?

(ii) How far from the origin is it at this time?

(iii) When does it next pass through the origin?

(iv) When is the object 1.5 m from the origin?

9 A tennis ball travelling vertically downwards with a speed of 5 ms^{-1} falls into a pond, where it experiences a deceleration of 2 ms^{-2}.

(i) Find the time the ball takes to come to rest.

(ii) Find how far below the surface of the pond the ball is at that point.

(iii) Assuming that the water resistance is constant, and that the ball is sufficiently buoyant to return to the surface with a uniform acceleration in 5 s, find its speed when it reaches the surface.

10 An airport has a straight runway of length 2000 m. During take-off, a light aircraft starting from rest and moving with a constant acceleration reaches its take-off speed of 120 km h^{-1} after 25 seconds.

(i) Express the take-off speed in ms^{-1}.

(ii) Find the acceleration during take-off in ms^{-2}.

(iii) Find the fraction of the length of the runway used by the aircraft during take-off.

11 Two stones are thrown vertically upwards from the same place with a 1 second interval, with an initial speed of $15\,\text{ms}^{-1}$. Taking g to be $10\,\text{ms}^{-2}$

(i) determine how long the first stone has been in the air when they collide.

(ii) find their velocities at the time of the collision.

Motion with variable acceleration

LEVEL 1

1 (i) If $s = 5t^2$ find v when $t = 2$.

(ii) If $v = 2t^2 + 3$ find a when $t = 3$.

(iii) If $s = t^3 - 2t + 1$ find a when $t = 4$.

2 If $v = 2t + 3$ and $s = 6$ when $t = 1$, find

(i) s in terms of t

(ii) the initial displacement.

3 If $v = 4t - 3t^2$ and the body is at O initially,

(i) find a in terms of t

(ii) find s in terms of t

(iii) what is the value of t when the body next passes O?

LEVEL 2

4 A particle starts from rest and moves along a straight line with acceleration $(6 + 6t)\,\text{ms}^{-2}$. After $1\,\text{s}$ it has travelled $10\,\text{m}$.

(i) Find v in terms of t.

(ii) Find s in terms of t.

(iii) Find the time when $v = 24$.

(iv) Find s at that time.

5 The velocity of a moving object at time t seconds is given by $v\,\text{ms}^{-1}$ where $v = 5t - t^2 - 6$.

  (i) Find the times when the object is i nstantaneously at rest.

  (ii) Find the acceleration at these times.

  (iii) What is the velocity when the acceleration is zero?

  (iv) Sketch the graph of v against t.

6 The height of a ball thrown vertically upwards is modelled by $h = 14t - 4.9t^2 + 1$.

  (i) Find an expression for the velocity of the ball.

  (ii) What is the time when the ball reaches its maximum height?

  (iii) What is the maximum height reached?

  (iv) Find the acceleration of the ball and comment on your result.

LEVEL 3

7 A particle moves along a straight line and t seconds after passing through the origin O its velocity is given by $v = c_1 t + c_2 t^2$ where c_1 and c_2 are constants.

When $t = 2$ the body is again at O and has an acceleration of $6\,\text{ms}^{-2}$.

  (i) Find an expression in terms of c_1, c_2 and t for the acceleration of the particle.

  (ii) Use this to find an equation connecting c_1 and c_2.

  (iii) Find an expression for the displacement $x\,\text{m}$ of the body at time t.

  (iv) Use this to find a second equation connecting c_1 and c_2.

  (v) Use the equations for **(ii)** and **(iv)** to find the velocity in terms of t.

8 Ellie is 12 years old and can run at $6\,\text{ms}^{-1}$. She has been entered for a 60 m race. A model is proposed where she accelerates uniformly to her maximum speed of $6\,\text{ms}^{-1}$ in 4 seconds, and then runs at her maximum speed for the rest of the distance. The diagram below shows the speed–time graph for this model.

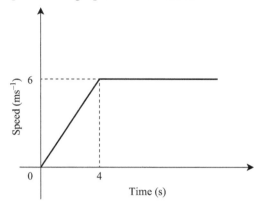

(i) Find the distance run in the first 4 seconds.

(ii) Find the total time taken to run the race.

Her teacher suggests an alternative model whereby for the first 4 seconds her speed $v\,\text{ms}^{-1}$ at time t seconds is given by the formula $v = \frac{3}{16}(6t^2 - t^3)$.

(iii) Find v when $t = 4$.

(iv) Show that the distance run in the first 4 seconds is the same as for the first model.

9 A skateboarder sets off from rest. His speed, t seconds after setting off, is $v\,\text{ms}^{-1}$, where $v = t - 0.05t^2$.

(i) Find when he is next at rest.

(ii) Calculate his initial acceleration.

(iii) Find an expression for his displacement at time t.

(iv) Given that this is measured from his starting point, calculate how far he has travelled before he is next at rest.

(v) Sketch a velocity–time graph for $0 \leqslant t \leqslant 20$ and indicate how the distance in **(iv)** is related to the graph.

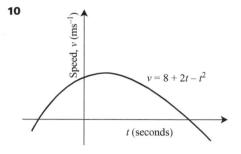

10

The sketch shows part of the velocity–time graph for the motion of an insect walking in a straight line. Its velocity $v\,\text{ms}^{-1}$ at time t seconds is given by $v = 8 + 2t - t^2$.

(i) Write down the velocity of the insect when $t = 0$.

(ii) Find when the insect is instantaneously at rest.

(iii) What happens next?

(iv) Find the maximum velocity of the insect.

(v) Calculate the distance travelled

    (a) in the first 4 seconds

    (b) in the first 5 seconds.

11 The displacement x m from the origin O of a particle on the x axis is given by $x = 4 + 8t + t^2 - t^3$, where t is the time in seconds and $0 \leqslant t \leqslant 4$.

(i) Write down the displacement when $t = 0$.

(ii) Find an expression, in terms of t, for the velocity $v\,\text{ms}^{-1}$ of the particle.

(iii) Find an expression, in terms of t, for the acceleration $a\,\text{ms}^{-2}$ of the particle.

(iv) Find the maximum velocity of the particle in the interval $0 \leqslant t \leqslant 4$.

(v) Find the value of t when $v = 0$ and also the value of x at this time.

(vi) Calculate the distance travelled by the particle in the first 2 seconds.

HINTS

Chapter 1

💡 EXERCISE 1.3, QUESTION 7

Let the two numbers be represented by x and y. Write down two simultaneous equations and solve them.

Chapter 2

💡 EXERCISE 2.1, QUESTION 5

Where necessary you need to start by collecting all the terms on the same side.

Chapter 4

💡 EXERCISE 4.1, QUESTION 7 (III)

Consider $x = 0.2$.

Chapter 5

💡 EXERCISE 5.1, QUESTION 9 (III)

Use OB as the base.

💡 EXERCISE 5.2, QUESTION 4

Find the distance between the origin and the centre.

Chapter 6

💡 EXERCISE 6.1, QUESTION 10

There are two possible solutions to this problem.

Chapter 7

💡 EXERCISE 7.1, QUESTION 6 (II)

Let $2\theta = x$ and start by solving $\cos x = 0.4$.

💡 EXERCISE 7.2, QUESTION 2

Part (i) gives you a value for $\cos^2\theta$. Remember that $\cos\theta$ can be positive or negative.

💡 EXERCISE 7.3, QUESTION 8

There are two right-angled triangles in the diagram that have the same base. Use 'sohcahtoa' in each of these.

Chapter 8

💡 EXERCISE 8.1, QUESTION 2 (III)

Put two wedges together to make a cuboid and find how many cuboids there are.

💡 EXERCISE 8.1, QUESTION 4 (III)

Don't forget that the rod has to be able to get through the door to get into the shed. The answer to this is **not** the longest diagonal.

💡 EXERCISE 8.1, QUESTION 5 (II)

Assume that the ski slope is wide enough for James to get from the top to the bottom without having to do any turns.

Chapter 9

💡 EXERCISE 9.1, QUESTION 10 (II)

Find a cubic equation and solve it using the factor theorem. You already know one factor if you think about it.

💡 EXERCISE 9.1, QUESTION 11 (II)

Parallel tangents have the same gradient, so you want another point on the curve with the same gradient as P.

💡 **EXERCISE 9.1, QUESTION 12 (V)**

The quadrilateral is made up of four right-angled triangles.

💡 **EXERCISE 9.2, QUESTION 3 (II)**

'No stationary points' means that the gradient is never zero.

💡 **EXERCISE 9.2, QUESTION 9**

Only consider values of x for which it is possible to construct the box.

Chapter 10

💡 **EXERCISE 10.2, QUESTION 10 (II)**

Use the information about the line of symmetry.

Chapter 11

💡 **EXERCISE 11.1, QUESTION 7 (III)**

You need two times while it is rising and then a third time while it falls to the ground.

💡 **EXERCISE 11.1, QUESTION 11 (II)**

Let the first stone be in the air for t seconds. For how long will the second stone be in the air?

💡 **EXERCISE 11.2, QUESTION 8 (II)**

Find how far there is left to run at her constant speed.

💡 **EXERCISE 11.2, QUESTION 10 (V) (B)**

Look what happens to the graph after $t = 4$ seconds.

ANSWERS

Chapter 1

EXERCISE 1.1

1 (i) $x + 6y$
  (ii) $x + 4y$
  (iii) $4a + 5b$

2 (i) $x + 5y$
  (ii) $3a^2 + 19a$
  (iii) $p^3 - p^2 - 2p$

3 (i) $2x(3 + 5x)$
  (ii) $3ab(b - 3a)$
  (iii) $3pq(4q - p^3)$

4 (i) $6a^2b^2c^2$
  (ii) $12x^3y^5$
  (iii) $\dfrac{x^2}{2y^3}$
  (iv) $\dfrac{3p^2}{2qr}$
  (v) $\dfrac{a}{12b^2}$

5 (i) $\dfrac{13x}{4}$
  (ii) $\dfrac{5s + 1}{4}$
  (iii) $\dfrac{16a}{15b}$

6 (i) $x = 8$
  (ii) $p = 3$

7 (i) $t = \dfrac{5s}{2}$
  (ii) $t = \dfrac{2s}{u + v}$
  (iii) $t = -5a$

8 (i) $(a + 21) = 7(a - 3)$
  (ii) 7 years

9 (i) $\theta + 50 + 78 = 180$
  (ii) $17°, 78°, 85°$

10 (i) $3(x + 4) = 5(x - 2); x = 11$
  (ii) $45\,\text{cm}^2$

11 (i) $6c - q - 20$
  (ii) $6c - 18 - 20 = 52; c = 15$

EXERCISE 1.2

1 (i) $a^2 - a - 6$
  (ii) $3x^2 + 10x - 8$
  (iii) $25 - 20x + 4x^2$

2 (i) $(a + 2)(a + 5)$
  (ii) $(x - 4)(x + 3)$
  (iii) $(p + 2)(p - 2)$
  (iv) $(3 + 2t)(3 - 2t)$
  (v) $(2c + 1)(c - 2)$
  (vi) $(3x + 1)(x - 3)$

3 (i) $2(x + 3)(x - 3)$
  (ii) $a(a - 4)(a - 5)$
  (iii) $ab(b + a)^2$

4 (i) $x = 4$ or $x = 5$
  (ii) $a = 2$ or $a = -2\frac{1}{4}$

5 (i) $x = -1 \pm \sqrt{2}$
  (ii) $a = 3 \pm \sqrt{21}$

6 (i) $x = 1.83$ or $x = -3.83$
  (ii) $x = 0.78$ or $x = -1.28$

7 (i) $a = 4$ or $a = \frac{2}{3}$
  (ii) $x = -4 \pm \sqrt{30}$ or $x = -9.48$ or $x = 1.48$
  (iii) $p = 0.72$ or $p = -1.39$

8 (i) $f(x) = (2x + 0.5)^2 - 3.25$
  (ii) Minimum value -3.25 when $x = -0.25$

9 (i) After 1 s and 3 s
  (ii) 4 s
  (iii) 4.05 s

10 (i) $\dfrac{165}{n}$
  (ii) $(n + 3)$ $\Rightarrow$ 3 more rows
      $\dfrac{165}{n} - 1$ $\Rightarrow$ 1 less in each row
      180 $\Rightarrow$ new total number of patches
  (iv) $n = 15$

11 (i) $c = 2$
  (ii)

  (iii) $k = -2$

(iv) Ammarah's model gives
$y = 2$ when $x = 2$
Anna's model gives
$y = -2$ when $x = 2$

EXERCISE 1.3

1 (i) $x = \frac{1}{3}, y = 1\frac{1}{3}$

(ii) $x = 3\frac{1}{2}, y = 2\frac{1}{2}$

2 (i) $x = 3, y = -1$
(ii) $x = 1, y = 2$

3 (i) $x = 1, y = 5$ or $x = -2.2, y = -4.6$
(ii) $x = 1, y = -5$ or $x = -2.6, y = 2.2$

4 $(2.89, 2.77)$ and $(-0.49, -3.97)$

5 £6.20

6 They represent parallel lines.

7 1.74 and 5.74

Chapter 2

EXERCISE 2.1

1 (i) $x < 4$

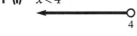

4

(ii) $a \leqslant 0.25$

0.25

(iii) $x \geqslant 15$

15

(iv) $p < 3$

3

2 (i)

0.25   3

(ii)

−1.5   1

(iii)

−7

3 (i)

−2   −1

(ii)

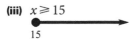

−0.25   0.75

4 (i) $2 < x < 2\frac{1}{3}$

(ii) $-\frac{2}{3} \leqslant x \leqslant 7\frac{1}{2}$

5 (i) $1 < x < 2$
(ii) $-\frac{1}{2} \leqslant a \leqslant 4$

(iii) $t < -1$ or $t > 3$
(iv) $x \leqslant 1$ or $x \geqslant 7$

EXERCISE 2.2

1 (i) $\dfrac{3}{3x+2}$

(ii) $\dfrac{x}{4y}$

(iii) $\dfrac{a-2}{a+2}$

2 (i) $\dfrac{2y^2}{15x}$

(ii) $\dfrac{2(x+1)}{(x+5)}$

(iii) $\dfrac{3(p-2)}{p(p+3)}$

3 (i) $\dfrac{5-2a}{a^2}$

(ii) $\dfrac{19p}{9}$

(iii) $\dfrac{5a}{6b}$

4 (i) $x - 6x^2$

(ii) $\dfrac{9p^3 + 81p^2 - 34}{9p}$

5 (i) $\dfrac{9}{2x+1}$

(ii) $\dfrac{3}{(3a-1)(a+2)}$

6 (i) $x = 3$
(ii) $p = 5$
(iii) $x = 3.23$ or $x = -0.80$

7 (i) $\dfrac{x-5}{x}$

(ii) $\dfrac{x-2}{x+3}$

(iii) $x = 12$

EXERCISE 2.3

1 (i) $3\sqrt{6}$
(ii) 4
(iii) $9 - 2\sqrt{3}$
(iv) $\sqrt{2}$

2 (i) $13 - 3\sqrt{5}$
(ii) $2 + \sqrt{2}$
(iii) $52 - 14\sqrt{3}$

3 (i) $2\sqrt{2}$

(ii) $\dfrac{3\sqrt{2}}{2}$

(iii) $\dfrac{\sqrt{2}}{4}$

(iv) $\dfrac{\sqrt{3}}{3}$

(v) $\dfrac{\sqrt{10}}{2}$

4 (i) $x = 2 \pm \sqrt{3}$

(ii) $x = \dfrac{-1 \pm \sqrt{6}}{2}$

(iii) $x = \dfrac{1 \pm \sqrt{3}}{2}$

Chapter 3

EXERCISE 3.1

1 (i) 3

(ii) 5

(iii) 2

2 (i) $6x^3 + 7x^2 - 3x - 16$

(ii) $x^4 - x^3 - x^2 + 2x - 2$

(iii) $5x^3 - 4x^2 + 18x - 22$

3 (i) $6x^3 - 11x^2 - 3x + 2$

(ii) $6x^6 + 10x^5 - 2x^4 - 9x^2 - 15x + 3$

4 (i) $2x^2 - 2x$

(ii) $x^3 - 12x^2 + x + 2$

5 (i) $x^2 + 3x + 2$

(ii) $2x^2 - 4x + 9$

EXERCISE 3.2

1 (ii) $(x-1)(x^2 - x - 6)$

(iii) $(x-1)(x-3)(x+2)$

2 $a = -10$

3 Remainder $= -24$

4 (i) $(x-2)(x^2 - x + 4)$

(ii) $(x+3)(x^2 + 1)$

(iii) $(x+2)(2x+1)(x+3)$

5 (i) $2x^2 + 7x + 1$

(ii) $2x^2 + 7x + 1$ doesn't factorise

6 $a = 2$ or $a = 3$

7 $a = \frac{1}{2}$ or $a = -1$

8 $a = 5$, $b = 2$; other factor is $x + 4$

9 $a = 0$, $b = -7$; other factor is $x + 3$

10 $a = -8\frac{1}{3}$, $b = 3\frac{1}{3}$

11 $x = 3$ or $x = 0.5$ or $x = -2$

12 (i) and (iii)

13 (i) $(x-1)(x-1)(x+3)$

(ii) A$(-3, 0)$, B$(1, 0)$, C$(0, 3)$

(iii) $(2\frac{1}{3}, 9\frac{13}{27})$

14 (i) (a) yes   (b) yes

(ii) $(x-2)(x-3)(x+5)$

(iii) $x = -5$; $x = 2$; $x = 3$

15 (i) $h = \dfrac{18}{x^2}$

(iv) $(x-3)$ is a factor

(v) $x = 3$ or $x = 3.62$ (2 d.p.)
reject $x = -6.62$
Possible dimensions are 3 m by 3 m by 2 m or 3.62 m by 3.62 m by 1.37 m.

Chapter 4

EXERCISE 4.1

1 (i) $1 + 8x + 24x^2 + 32x^3 + 16x^4$

(ii) $1 - 9x + 27x^2 - 27x^3$

(iii) $1 + 5x^2 + 10x^4 + 10x^6 + 5x^8 + x^{10}$

(iv) $x^4 + 12x^3 + 54x^2 + 108x + 81$

(v) $x^3 + 6x^2 y + 12xy^2 + 8y^3$

(vi) $16x^4 - 96x^3 y + 216x^2 y^2 - 216xy^3 + 81y^4$

2 (i) -160

(ii) 720

(iii) -960

3 $3x + 9x^2 + 7x^3$

4 $1 - 9x + 27x^2 - 27x^3$
$2 - 19x + 63x^2 - 81x^3 + 27x^4$

5 (i) $x^3 + 6x^2 + 12x + 8$

(ii) $x = 0$ or $x = -2$

6 (i) $1 + 12x + 60x^2 + 160x^3$

(ii) $x = 0.01$; $1.02^6 \approx 1.12616$

(iii) True value 1.126162419 so (ii) is correct to 6 s.f.

7 (i) and (ii)

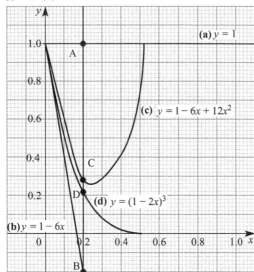

(a) $y = 1$

(c) $y = 1 - 6x + 12x^2$

C

D (d) $y = (1 - 2x)^3$

(b) $y = 1 - 6x$

B

(iii) **(a)** 0.784
(b) 0.416
(c) 0.064

8 (i) $16 - 32x + 24x^2$
(ii) Yes; at (8, 1296)
(iii) $0 \leqslant x \leqslant 0.5$

9 (i) **(a)** $x = 0$ and $x = 4$
(b) (2, 6.4)
(iii) 437.5 m

1 (i) $\frac{1}{6}$
(ii) $\frac{1}{36}$
(iii) $\frac{19}{144}$

2 (i) $\frac{5}{6}$
(ii) 0.054 (3 d.p.)

3 0.137 (3 d.p.)

4 (i) 0.122 (3 d.p.)
(ii) 0.285 (3 d.p.)
(iii) 0.677 (3 d.p.)

5 (i) 8
(ii) 0.376 (3 d.p.)

6 (i) 0.668 (3 d.p.)
(ii) 0.007 (3 d.p.)

7 (i) 0.078 (3 d.p.)
(ii) 0.088 (3 d.p.)
(iii) 0.683 (3 d.p.)

8 0.104 (3 d.p.)

9 (i) 0.376
(ii) **(a)** 0.469 **(b)** 0.611
(iii) 5 goes

10 (i) 0.85076
(ii) 0.13890
(iii) 10 trays
(iv) 0.00356

Chapter 5

1 (i) $\frac{4}{3}$
(ii) $-\frac{3}{4}$
(iii) 10
(iv) (2, 7)

2 $AB = BC = 5$, $AC = \sqrt{50}$ so isosceles

3 (i) 3
(ii) $\frac{1}{5}$
(iii) $-\frac{2}{3}$

4 (i) $y = 5x - 14$
(ii) $x + y = -2$
(iii) $3x - 2y = 14$

5 (i) $x + 4y = 1$
(ii) $x + 2y + 1 = 0$
(iii) $y = 4x + 13$

6 (i) $x + 5y = 0$
(ii) $x + y + 1 = 0$
(iii) $7x + y = 20$

7 (i)

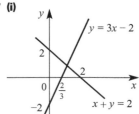

Point (1, 1)

(ii)

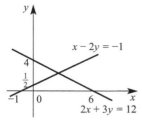

Point (3, 2)

(iii)

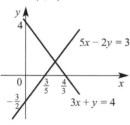

Point (1, 1)

8 (i)

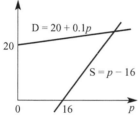

(ii) £40; 24 articles

9 (i)

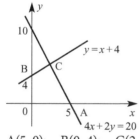

(ii) A(5, 0); B(0, 4); C(2, 6)
(iii) 4 units^2
(iv) (7, 2)

1 (i) $(x-1)^2+(y-1)^2=4$
(ii) $(x-2)^2+(y-5)^2=9$
(iii) $(x+1)^2+(y+4)^2=25$
2 (i) Radius 2, centre (-1, 2)

(ii)

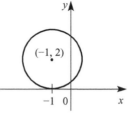

3 Rearranges to $(x+2)^2+(y-1)^2=4$
Radius 2, centre (-2, 1)

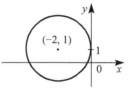

4 Origin is inside
5 (i) No point of intersection
(ii) Line is a tangent
6 (i)

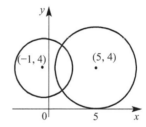

Points $\left(\frac{17}{12}, 4 \pm \frac{\sqrt{455}}{12}\right)$
(ii) They are perpendicular
(iii) Yes

Chapter 6

1 (i)

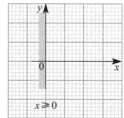

$x \geqslant 0$

(ii)

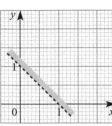

(iii)

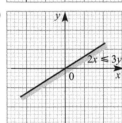

5

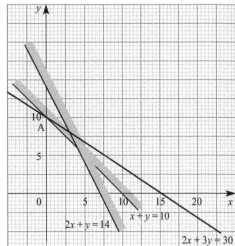

Max value at $(0, 10) \Rightarrow$ value $= 30$

6 (i) $a \geqslant 0, c \geqslant 0, a + c \leqslant 500,$
$c \geqslant \frac{500}{3}, c \geqslant 167$ (whole number)

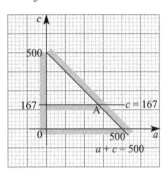

(ii) $P = 8a + 5c$

(iii) £3499

7 (i) Number of wheels available
$3x + 2y \leqslant 1200$

(ii)

2 (i)

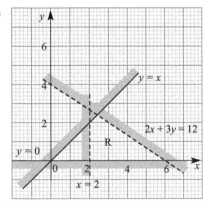

(ii) no

3 $x \geqslant 0, y \geqslant 0, y < 2, x + y < 4$

4 (i)

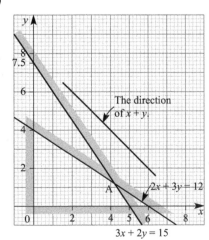

(ii) 5.4

(iii) $C = 50x + 30y$

(iv) 200 prams, 300 pushchairs
£2700 = max income

8 (i) Restriction of 80 hours labour;
$2x + 3y \leqslant 150$

(ii)

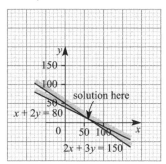

(iii) Profit $p = 10x + 18y$

(iv) 60 type A, 10 type B;
Profit = £780

9 (i) $0 \leqslant s \leqslant 11; 0 \leqslant f \leqslant 10;$
$f \leqslant s \leqslant \dfrac{4f}{3}$

(ii)

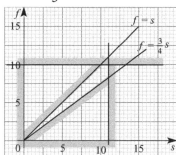

(iii) (a) $(11, 10)$ **(b)** $(10, 10)$
(c) $(11, 8\frac{3}{4})$ **(d)** $(6, 4\frac{1}{2})$

10 7 large vans and no small ones, or
6 large and 2 small

Chapter 7

EXERCISE 7.1

1 (i) 2.3 cm
(ii) 3.6 cm

2 (i) 26.4°
(ii) 47.4°

3 (i) 178 m
(ii) 91 m

4 (i) 11.5°, 168.5°
(ii) 30°, 330°
(iii) 76.0°, 256.0°
(iv) 224.4°, 315.6°

(v) 154.2°, 205.8°
(vi) 135°, 315°

5 (i) 199.5°, 340.5°
(ii) 41.4°, 318.6°

6 (i) 66.4°, 293.6°
(ii) 33.2°, 146.8°

7 31.7°, 121.7°

8 −135°, −76.0°, 45°, 104.0°

EXERCISE 7.2

1 (i) $\tan \theta = \frac{1}{2}$
(ii) −153.4°, 26.6°

2 (i) $3 \cos^2\theta = 2$
(ii) 35.3°, 144.7°, 215.3°, 324.7°

3 −270°, −90°, 90°, 270°

4 (63.4°, 0.9)

5 120°, 240°

6 54.7°, 125.3°, 234.7°, 305.3°

EXERCISE 7.3

1 (i) 4.7 cm
(ii) 4.2 cm

2 (i) 52.9°
(ii) 49.5°

3 (i) 8.9 cm^2
(ii) 8.0 cm^2

4 13.8 km

5 (i) 13°
(ii) 187.9 m
(iii) 39.1 m

6 (i) 8.2 cm and 15.8 cm
(ii) 58.4 cm^2

7 (i) 036°
(ii) 4811 m^2

8 74 m

9 (i)

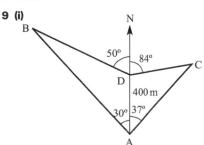

(ii) 896 m

(iii) 853 m

10 (i) $\angle LAB = 60°$

$\angle LBA = 70°$

(ii) $AB = 4.08\,km$

(iii) $8.2\,km\,h^{-1}$

Chapter 8

EXERCISE 8.1

1 (i) 15 cm

(ii) 18.4°

(iii) 13 cm

(iv) 34.7°

2 (i) 3.2 cm

(ii) 116 cm³

(iii) 480

3 (i) 61.9°

(ii) 69.3°

4 (i) 26.6°

(ii) 20 m³

(iii) 5.2 m

5 (i) 25.9 m

(ii) 297 m

6 (i) 3.15 m and 3.73 m

(ii) 14.8° and 17.6°

7 (i) 914 m from A and 761 m from B

(ii) 541 m

(iii) 535 m

Chapter 9

EXERCISE 9.1

1 (i) $\dfrac{dy}{dx} = 5x^4$

(ii) $\dfrac{dy}{dx} = 21x^6$

(iii) $\dfrac{dy}{dx} = 0$

(iv) $\dfrac{dy}{dx} = 18x^8 - 6x$

(v) $\dfrac{dy}{dx} = 9x^5 + 2$

(vi) $\dfrac{dy}{dx} = -x^2$

(vii) $\dfrac{dv}{dt} = 6t^2$

(viii) $\dfrac{dV}{dr} = 4\pi r^2$

(ix) $\dfrac{ds}{dt} = 4t - 4$

(x) $\dfrac{dy}{dx} = 4x + 5$

(xi) $\dfrac{dy}{dx} = 3x^2 - 2x + 1$

(xii) $\dfrac{dy}{dx} = 32x + 8$

2 $k = 2$

3 (i) $f'(x) = 3x^2 - 2x + 2$

(ii) 18

4 (i) $\dfrac{dy}{dx} = 3x^2 - 12x + 2$

(ii) −7

(iii) $y = -7x + 19$

(iv) $x - 7y + 83 = 0$

5 (i) $\dfrac{dy}{dx} = 9 - 3x^2$

(ii) 6

(iii) $y = 6x - 2$

(iv) $x + 6y + 49 = 0$

6 (i) $\dfrac{dy}{dx} = 3x^2 - 6x$

(ii) 0

(iii) $y = -5$

(iv) $x = 0$

7 (i) $y = 9x - 16$

(iii) −52

8 (i) $2x + y - 15 = 0$

(ii) $x - 2y = 0$

9 (i) $\dfrac{dy}{dx} = 3x^2 - 10x + 6$

(ii) Point $(0, 0)$, gradient = 6

Point $(2, 0)$, gradient = −2

Point $(3, 0)$, gradient = 3

10 (i) $y = x - 7$

(ii) $(-2, -9)$

11 (i) $y = 11x - 33$

(ii) $-\frac{5}{3}$

12 (i) $\dfrac{dy}{dx} = 3x^2 + 6x - 7$

(ii) P(1, –7) Q(–3, 17)

(iii) Tangent at P: $y = 2x - 9$
Tangent at Q: $y = 2x + 23$

(iv) 256 units^2

(v) Trapezium

EXERCISE 9.2

1 (i) (a) $\dfrac{dy}{dx} = 3x^2 - 12x$, $x = 0, 4$

(b) $x = 0$, max; $x = 4$, min

(c) max $(0, 4)$; min $(4, -28)$

(d)

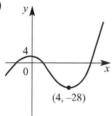

(ii) (a) $\dfrac{dy}{dx} = 4x^3 - 16x$, $x = -2, 0, 2$

(b) $x = -2$, min; $x = 0$, max; $x = 2$, min

(c) min $(-2, 0)$; max $(0, 16)$; min $(2, 0)$

(d)

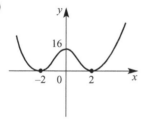

(iii) (a) $\dfrac{dy}{dx} = 9 + 6x - 3x^2$, $x = -1, 3$

(b) $x = -1$, min; $x = 3$, max

(c) min $(-1, -5)$; max $(3, 27)$

(d)

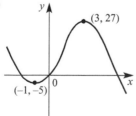

(iv) (a) $\dfrac{dy}{dx} = 4x^3 - 12x^2$, $x = 0, 3$

(b) $x = 0$, point of inflection;
$x = 3$, min

(c) point of inflection $(0, 6)$;
min $(3, -21)$

(d)

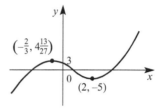

2 (i) max $(-\frac{2}{3}, 4\frac{13}{27})$; min $(2, -5)$

(ii)

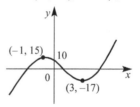

3 (i) $a + b = -2$; $2a + b = -7$; $a = -5$, $b = 3$

4 max $(-2, 11)$, min $(\frac{2}{3}, -\frac{14}{27})$

5 (i) $p = -9$, $q = 10$

(ii) max $(-1, 15)$; min $(3, -17)$

(iii)

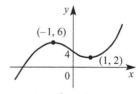

6 (i) max $(-1, 6)$; min $(1, 2)$

(ii)

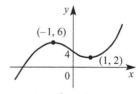

(iii) $x < -1$ and $x > 1$

(iv) $-1 < x < 1$

7 (i) $b = 3a - a^4$

(ii) $3a^3 - 3 = 0$

(iii) $a = 1$, $b = 2$

8 (i) $a - 8b + 16c = 20$; $a = 4$

(ii) $12b - 32c = 0$

(iii) $a = 4$, $b = -8$, $c = -3$

Answers

(iv)

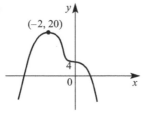

9 max volume $= 18\,\text{cm}^3$ when $x = 1$

Chapter 10

EXERCISE 10.1

1 (i) $y = 2x^2 - 2x + c$

(ii) $y = x^3 + x^2 - x + c$

(iii) $y = 5x + c$

(iv) $f(x) = \dfrac{x^4}{4} - x^3 + x + c$

(v) $f(x) = \dfrac{x^3}{3} - 2x^2 + 4x + c$

(vi) $f(x) = 4x - x^2 + c$

2 (i) $x^3 + c$

(ii) $\dfrac{2x^5}{5} - x^3 + 4x + c$

(iii) $\dfrac{x^3}{3} - x + c$

(iv) $5x + x^2 + c$

(v) $\dfrac{x^3}{3} - x^2 + x + c$

(vi) $4x + c$

3 (i) $y = x^2 + 4x - 5$

(ii) $y = \dfrac{x^3}{3} + x + 16$

(iii) $f(x) = \dfrac{x^3}{3} + x^2 + x - 23$

(iv) $f(x) = \dfrac{x^3}{3} - x - 4$

4 (i) $y = 2x^2 - 3x + c$

(ii) $y = 2x^2 - 3x$

5 (i) $f(x) = x^3 - 3x^2 - 4x - 2$

(ii) $(-1, -2), (0, -2), (4, -2)$

6 (i) $x = \pm 1$

(ii) $y = 2x^3 - 6x + 3$

(iii)

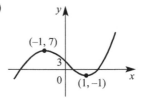

7 (i) $y = x^3 - x^2 - x + 1$

(ii) $(1, 0)$ and $\left(-\tfrac{1}{3}, 1\tfrac{5}{27}\right)$

(iii)

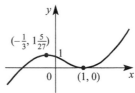

EXERCISE 10.2

1 (i) $2\tfrac{1}{3}$

(ii) 33

(iii) 24

2 (i) 8

(ii) 18

(iii) 42

(iv) 36

(v) $-1\tfrac{1}{3}$

(vi) 45

3 (i) $4\tfrac{2}{3}\,\text{units}^2$

(ii) $3\tfrac{3}{4}\,\text{units}^2$

(iii) $\tfrac{4}{27}\,\text{units}^2$

(iv) $2\tfrac{2}{3}\,\text{units}^2$

4 $10\tfrac{2}{3}\,\text{units}^2$

5 (i) A: $4\,\text{units}^2$; B: $4\,\text{units}^2$

(ii) 0

(iii) Areas above and below the x axis have cancelled out

6 (i)

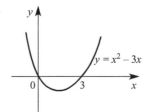

(ii) $0 \leqslant x \leqslant 3$

(iii) $4\frac{1}{2}$ units² below x axis

7 (i)

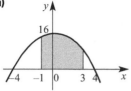

(ii) $54\frac{2}{3}$ units²

8 (i) A(−1, 1); B(7, 17)

(ii) $85\frac{1}{3}$ units²

9 (i) $y = -4x + 8$

(ii) $2\frac{2}{3}$ units²

10 (i) $y = 1 - x$

(ii) 3 units²

(iii) 4800 cm²

11 (i) $3\frac{5}{6}$ units²

(ii) $408\frac{1}{3}$ m³

Chapter 11

EXERCISE 11.1

1 (i) $v = u + at$

(ii) $v^2 = u^2 + 2as$

(iii) $s = ut + \frac{1}{2}at^2$

(iv) $s = \dfrac{(u+v)}{2}t$

2 (i) $s = 5$

(ii) $t = 12\frac{1}{2}$

(iii) $a = 2$

(iv) $v = -3$; travelling in the opposite direction to the initial motion

(v) $u = -3\frac{1}{2}$; sets off in the negative direction

3 (i) $t = 1.28$ s

(ii) $v = 12.5$ ms⁻¹

4 2.45 s

5 1.25 ms⁻²

6 (i) 1.25 ms⁻²

(ii) 162.5 m

7 (i) 40 ms⁻¹

(ii) 181.6 m

(iii) 15.16 s

8 (i) 1.6 s

(ii) 6.4 m

(iii) After 3.2 s

(iv) After 0.2 s and 3 s

9 (i) 2.5 s

(ii) 6.25 m

(iii) 2.5 ms⁻¹

10 (i) $33\frac{1}{3}$ ms⁻¹

(ii) $1\frac{1}{3}$ ms⁻²

(iii) $\frac{5}{24}$

11 (i) 2 s

(ii) Stone 1: 5 ms⁻¹ downwards; stone 2: 5 ms⁻¹ upwards

EXERCISE 11.2

1 (i) 20

(ii) 12

(iii) 24

2 (i) $s = t^2 + 3t + 2$

(ii) 2 m

3 (i) $a = 4 - 6t$

(ii) $s = 2t^2 - t^3$

(iii) $t = 2$

4 (i) $v = 6t + 3t^2$

(ii) $s = 3t^2 + t^3 + 6$

(iii) 2 s

(iv) 26 m

5 (i) 2 s and 3 s

(ii) $t = 2 \Rightarrow a = 1$ ms⁻²; $t = 3 \Rightarrow a = -1$ ms⁻²

(iii) 0.25 ms⁻¹

(iv)

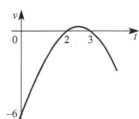

6 (i) $v = 14 - 9.8t$

(ii) After $1\frac{3}{7}$ s

(iii) 11 m

(iv) $a = -9.8$; acceleration due to gravity

7 (i) $a = c_1 + 2c_2 t$

(ii) $6 = c_1 + 4c_2$

(iii) $x = \dfrac{c_1 t^2}{2} + \dfrac{c_2 t^3}{3}$

(iv) $2c_1 + \frac{8}{3}c_2 = 0$

(v) $v = \frac{9}{4}t^2 - 3t$

8 (i) 12 m

(ii) 12 s

(iii) $6\,\text{ms}^{-1}$

9 (i) After 20 s

(ii) $1\,\text{ms}^{-2}$

(iii) $s = \dfrac{t^2}{2} - \dfrac{t^3}{60}$

(iv) $66\frac{2}{3}$ m

(v)

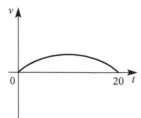

Distance = area between the curve and the t axis.

10 (i) $8\,\text{ms}^{-1}$

(ii) After 4 s

(iii) It changes direction

(iv) $9\,\text{ms}^{-1}$

(v) **(a)** $26\frac{2}{3}$ m   **(b)** 30 m

11 (i) 4 m

(ii) $v = 8 + 2t - 3t^2$

(iii) $a = 2 - 6t$

(iv) $8\frac{1}{3}\,\text{ms}^{-1}$

(v) $t = 2,\ x = 16$

(vi) 12 m